artists/**USA**
1979-80

artists/**USA**
NINETEEN

SEVENTY NINE-EIGHTY

published by
THE FOUNDATION FOR THE ADVANCEMENT OF ARTISTS

Herbert Lieberman, Publisher
Howard Jeffries, Editor

3

Dedicated to
the memory of:
MIRIAM SADEL LIEBERMAN

COPYRIGHT © 1979 by
THE FOUNDATION FOR THE ADVANCEMENT OF ARTISTS

PUBLISHED IN THE UNITED STATES OF AMERICA
THE FOUNDATION FOR THE ADVANCEMENT OF ARTISTS
P.O. BOX 11617, PHILADELPHIA, PA. 19116

ISBN #0-912916-06-0
LIBRARY OF CONGRESS CATALOG #78-134303

SIXTH EDITION

PRINTED IN THE UNITED STATES OF AMERICA

CONTENTS

ABBREVIATIONS

Am — American
Arch — Architecture
Assn — Association
Coll — Collection
Exbt — Exhibit
Exbtn — Exhibition
Fed — Federation
Fdn — Foundation
Hon Men — Honorable Mention
Inst — Institute
Intl — International
Invit — Invitational
Mod — Modern
Natl — National
NFS — Not for Sale
POR — Price on Request
Priv — Private
Prof — Professional
Publ — Public
Regl — Regional
Sculp — Sculpture
Soc — Society
Univ — University

FOREWORD

by Herbert Lieberman
Publisher

"Every genuine work of art
has as much reason for being
as the earth and the sun."
—Ralph Waldo Emerson

The art industry is booming. Today, it is rare for an individual not to have an original piece of art or a reproduction somewhere in his or her home and office. High quality reproductions are available like never before and at prices within most budgets. There are more collectors than ever, and no longer is it considered a preoccupation reserved only for the affluent. So why does the concept of "the starving artist" remain more a reality than a cliché?

Unfortunately, even in this day of electronic, "space age" communications and mass marketing, the average artist has little opportunity to be seen outside of his own community. Becoming "established" and maintaining that desirous position continues to be a difficult problem for the professional artist. An artist in a small town will usually remain an artist in a small town, his works seldom being viewed outside the confines of his geographic locale. Certainly the artist's problems are compounded by the very nature of his work—While the creative fruits of a writer are easily duplicated and reproduced with no loss of substance or meaning, most forms of fine art are not so easily copied for distribution. And even once this obstacle is cleared, there are few mass marketing techniques available for the artwork. It is, indeed, a rather arduous task for the serious art collector or occasional buyer to see a genuine representation of America's currently-produced art. Thus, tragically, the works of the great majority of professional artists go unseen by this vast audience.

It was with this in mind that ARTISTS/USA was born in 1969. Eliminating once-insurmountable problems of geography and filling a serious void in the art world, ARTISTS/USA brings together hundreds of living world famous, locally-known and newly-emerging talents from all parts of the United States into one permanent volume. It is a publication by and for artists. No arbitrary limitations or personal preferences are imposed on them. They select their own works to exhibit and establish their own prices. Through international sales and distribution, ARTISTS/USA has opened up the world to the American artist.

In addition, ARTISTS/USA serves as an historical compendium of one moment in the long annuls of art, and comparison with previous editions may offer some clues to both artistic and social changes . . . and future trends. For artists have always held a special position in society, being the most receptive to subtle societal discontentments and growth, their sensitivities bringing such matters to the fore to be perceived by others. It is, thus, with great pride that we present the contemporary American artist—ARTISTS/USA 1979-80.

Society's Step-Children

by Dixie Burrus Browning

EDITOR'S NOTE: Dixie Burrus Browning is the author of 5 novels and several articles on art. She is the first president of the Watercolor Society of North Carolina and is listed in Who's Who in American Art *and* World Who's Who of Women.

Art has long been the darling of society; individual artists, all too often, the step-children. This is more fortunate than one might suppose, for were artists to embrace the values, the mores of society, their most important function would be seriously compromised. No longer would they retain the objectivity necessary to act as barometers, signaling the unrest that precedes change, to see with unerring clarity the condition of man in his universe.

Neither esoteric nor mundane, art, according to Robert Henri, is "an extension of language to the expression of sensations too subtle for words."* Good art refines the atmosphere around it. Its ambience is positive, constructive. It can create a hiatus in the here and now, staying the flow of adrenalin, slowing the pulse, allowing the flow of harmony, beauty, and order that need not be fully understood intellectually to be felt and appreciated.

Regardless of the particular "ism" imposed on it by those whose duty it is to verbalize, art finds and records the order and beauty in a world that has gathered too much momentum. Even in the most discordant-seeming work of art there is an underlying cohesive structure, if the work is successful, that gives silent evidence of the unique ability of the artist to rise above the level of society and see patterns where none are apparent, order where none is evident, harmony and beauty in what appears at eye-level to be hopeless chaos.

Simplistically, one might say that the purpose of artists is to create art. The work of a single artist is a record of one man's journey through this lifetime, of the things he sees, feels and senses along the way, recorded in whatever language he speaks best, be it paint, stone, music or words. His skill in his chosen language determines how truly he reveals his findings.

Some art is the product of those who would not call themselves artists. The ostensibly haphazard patches on a quilt, an arrangement of cabbages and roses against the burnt sienna earth. An artist digs a ditch across a plain, and a farmer digs a ditch across a pasture. One is considered art, the other, drainage. Andy Warhol satirizes and the world takes him seriously. Art imitates life imitates art.

The art of a prehistoric people is all that remains today to mark their existence, other than the continuity of man, himself. Today that art is considered highly portentous. If one could transpose the doodles from the telephone pad to the walls of a distant cave, no doubt theories, esoteric and profound, would arise relating them to forces invoked, repelled, to elements about which the artist's life revolved. Who can say which is the more valid art form, the doodles or the cave drawings?

Fashions in art change, as witness the storage rooms of many museums, filled with "outgrown, unfashionable" art. Consider the relative positions of Bouguereau and Cezanne, both now and during their lifetimes.

Museums today exhibit primitive art and recently, at least one museum showed a collection of art done by those ladies of the nineteenth and early twentieth century who were of a social and financial position that enabled them to become "trained" in the popular modes of the day: the watercolor, the oil on velvet, tinfoil, glass, and needlework.

Today more and more people have the means to pursue creative avocations. Training is readily available to a far wider spectrum of society, and both verbal and visual world-wide communication is taken for granted, possibly creating a homogenizing effect on much of the art being produced.

It will be interesting to see how the future looks on today's art. Some of what we consider our most sophisticated work may be designated by future critics and chroniclers as folk art, as the twentieth century equivalent of the work done by those lovely Victorian and Edwardian ladies whose pale hands were kept suitably busy with brush and needle. Therefore, it seems pointless for an artist to over-concern himself with his own work much beyond its creation.

Long after the slick magazines and newspapers with their erudite discourses on art have crumbled away, the art, itself, will remain. Critics, judges, and merchandisers can modify the material value of a work of art for awhile, but only the perspective of time can determine the intrinsic value of a work, and even then, not all art will speak to the same people.

Universal truths notwithstanding, people speak different languages. At any given time in the world, all rungs of the ladder of evolution are filled. Among those at every level of development are the artists, who see, feel, and are compelled to translate their visions, their feelings into a language of their own. While the message may not be evident to those on higher or lower rungs, it is of inestimable value to those around them who speak the same language as the artist.

In one sense, perhaps the most important sense, art is the act of creation, itself; the conception and execution of the original idea. The resulting work is a by-product. The terrifying, exhilarating struggle to give tangible form to an intangible idea is the artist's truest reward. At its best, art is a product of all levels of consciousness and may, in time, reveal the artist to himself, even as it meets every viewer with its gift.

Good art, in every style, every medium, can act as a mirror to reflect back to the viewer aspects of the soul only dimly sensed. It is a strengthening, reassuring force that reaffirms the existence of order, beauty, and harmony at a time when man may be in danger of losing his way.

*Robert Henri, *The Art Spirit,* J.B. Lippincott Company

artists/USA
1979 - 80

ADDAMS, CHARLES
℅ New Yorker Magazine
25 W. 43rd Street
New York, N.Y. 10036

BORN:
    Westfield, N.J., Jan. 7, 1912

EXHIBITIONS:
    Fogg Art Museum
    Metropolitan Museum of Art, N.Y.
    Museum of the City of New York
    Pa. State University Museum
    Rhode Island School of Design
    and many others

Charles Addams works in India ink
and watercolors.

"BOYS AND GIRLS COME OUT TO PLAY" 20¾" x 16"
Gouache, wash, brush, pen and ink on paper mounted on cardboard sheet
Collection, The Museum of Modern Art, New York
Gift of the artist

AASEN, ARNE
1011 Howard St.
San Francisco, Calif.

AILES, CURTIS A.
R.R. #5 Country Brook
Connersville, Ind. 47331

GALLERY:
Hoosier Salon Art Gallery
951 N. Delaware
Indianapolis, Ind. 46202

EXHIBITIONS:
Hoosier Salon Art Gallery
Evansville Museum, Ind.
Fireside Arts Gallery, Ind.
Sheldon Swope Gallery, Ind.
White Water Valley Art Assn,
Connersville, Ind.

Brown County Art Gallery,
Nashville, Ind.
Indianapolis Museum of Art,
Downtown Gallery

AWARDS:
Many local & natl
Purchase Awards

COLLECTIONS:
Many private & public
worldwide including:
Former Pres. Richard Nixon

"SUNDAY MORNING" 22" x 28" Oil $875.

ABBATECOLA, ORONZO
3095 Greentree Way
San Jose, Calif. 95128

GALLERY:
deMetafisica
3095 Greentree Way
San Jose, Calif. 95128

EXHIBITIONS:
Bari, Rome, Naples, Milan,
Florence, Genoa, Venice
Vienna, Austria
Paris, France
Warsaw, Poland
South America & U.S.

AWARDS:
Rome, Genoa, Florence,
& Venice, Italy
Los Angeles, San Francisco,
Los Gatos, Calif.

COLLECTIONS:
Rome & Venice, Italy
Vienna, Austria
Hyde Park
Triton Museum of Art
Santa Clara, Calif.
Abbatecola Museum, Calif.

"CAPRICCIO ITALIANO" Scale Model

"LETTER 'J' FROM THE SERIES: THE EVOLUTION OF THE
ALPHABET" 30" x 50" Oil on Canvas

ARTISTS/USA

"SEARCHING" 1978 16" x 20" Charcoal POR

ANDERSON, LILLIAN Y.
Box 1004
Oak Bluff, Mass. 02557

BORN:
Luneville, France, 1945

EXHIBITIONS:
Numerous one-artist and
group shows

AWARDS:
Martha's Vineyard Island Fair

COLLECTIONS:
Rev. J.F. D'Amico, Sacred
Heart Rectory, Oak Bluff
Rev. H.A. Waldron,
Somerset, Mass.
Shiretown Inn Hotel,
Edgartown
Square Rigger Restaurant,
Edgartown
Mr. & Mrs. Jean Ferry, France
Dr. R.M. Johnson, Sacramento
and many other private colls.

"THE VIRGIN IN SORROW" 1978 22" x 34" Oil POR   "CHRIST CARRYING THE CROSS" 1978 20" x 30" Oil POR

ALBERTS, COL. ROBERT L.

101 Harbor Lane
Massapequa Park, N.Y. 11762

EXHIBITIONS:
Many group shows in U.S. & Canada

AWARDS:
Gold Medal & Certificate of Chevalier
for the Arts and Humanities Sociate
Nationale Francaise
Wanamaker Competition, Gold Medal
and many others

COLLECTIONS:
Trinity College, Ontario, Canada
N.Y. University, N.Y.C.
Army/Navy Legion of Valor
Lt. Gen. Burt Fay, USMC
Mr. & Mrs. Theo Novak, Northport
Mr. & Mrs. S. Raffles, Miami, Fla.
Dr. Ralph Marcove, N.Y.C.
Dr. Mortimer Lasky, Miami, Fla.
Brig. Gen. & Mrs. Arnold Alberts,
Massapequa Park, N.Y.
Mr. & Mrs. Samuel Schreiber, Purchase, N.Y.
Mr. & Mrs. Irwin Raboy, Harrison, N.Y.
Mr. & Mrs. David Alberts, Harbor Greens, L.I.
Mr. & Mrs. Milton Safane, Cliffside Park, N.J.
Msgr. Patrick Fay
Sir Vincenzo Berlinger, Genoa, Italy
Incres Steamship Lines, Genoa
Order of LaFayette, N. Y. C.
and many other private collections

"THE RUSSIAN" 18" x 24"

"MSGR. PATRICK FAY" 30" x 40"

"MRS. ROBERT ALBERTS" 18" x 24"

''BERTRAND T. FAY, Lt. Gen. USMCR Ret.'' 30" x 40"

"SELF PORTRAIT" 1977 18" x 24" Acrylics on Linen NFS

ANICHINI, MARIO
Rt. 4, Box 393-C
Antioch, Illinois 60002

Mario Anichini has evolved through many different works in a fresh new kind of impressionism which borders on the limits of imagination, and beyond the limits of reality.

He is included in the 16th edition of *Who's Who in the Midwest, Who's Who in America* and *ARTISTS/USA 1977-78.*

"SPIRIT OF ST. LOUIS" 1978 30" x 40" Acrylics on Linen
Collection of Mr. G. Cumberland, Mundelein, Illinois

"PAUL REVERE" 1975 18½" x 19½" x 7" Bronze (Lost Wax Method) Limited edition of 6 POR

ANICHINI, MARIO

"LIFE" 1973 18½" x 14½" x 6" Solid Cast Aluminum POR

"EVOLUTION" 1973 24" x 36" Acrylics on Canvas NFS

"MERRY-GO-ROUND" 30" x 40" Oil POR

ALDEN, SELMA
66 Maynard St.
W. Newton, Mass. 02165

GALLERIES:
Cambridge Art Assoc.
  Cambridge, Mass. 02138
Copley Society
  Boston, Mass. 02116
Home Studio & Gallery

Although Selma Alden attended the Museum School and Vesper George School of Art, she is mainly self-taught. She has continued her education with George Guzzi, illustrator, George Dergalis, King Coffin at the DeCordova Museum and John Bageris. She specializes in people, places and things, using acrylic, oil and pen and ink almost exclusively. Her drawings and paintings are in many offices and private collections in New York and New England.

"DISH STUDY" 36" x 36" Acrylic POR

"TEMPLE ONE" 9' x 6' x 12½"
Acrylic, Wood & Canvas POR

ARMSTRONG, SARA G.
3819 Redmont Road
Birmingham, Ala. 35213

EXHIBITIONS:
1st Ala. Invitational-1978
Natl. Sculpture, Columbia, S.C.-1978
4 Ala. Artists Working on Paper, U.A.B. Visual Arts Gallery-1978

Intl Women's Year Touring Exhibition-1977
One-artist shows:
U.A.B. Visual Arts Gallery-1977
Memorial Theatre, Louisville, Ky.-1977

COLLECTIONS:
Public & private colls. in the Southeast

ATKIN, EDITH
2500 North Gate Terrace
Silver Spring, Maryland 20906

BORN:
Washington, D.C.

GALLERY:
Lynn Kottler Gallery
3 E. 65th St., New York, N.Y.

"THE DREAMER" 24" x 36" Oil POR

"SPONTANEOUS PATIENCE"
Found Object Assemblage with
Shadows, POR © Be Art 1977–78
As seen in Lincoln Center, N.Y.C.

ARTHUR, BRADLEY D.
211 E. Davis Blvd.
Tampa, Florida 33606

BORN:
Tampa, Florida

EXHIBITIONS:
Lincoln Center, Avery Fisher
    Hall, N.Y.C.
Womanart Galleries, N.Y.C.
Lynn Kottler Galleries, N.Y.C.

Tampa Bay Art Center, Fla.
The Art Center, St. Petersburg
Arts Festival '76, Bicentennial
    Show, Tampa
U.S.F., 1-artist show:
    "Pieces so Far"
Univ. of S. Fla., 1-artist
Hollywood Museum, Fla.
Sculptors of Florida Show

GALLERY:
Lynn Kottler Galleries
    3 E. 65th St.
    New York, N.Y. 10021
Womanart Galleries
    41 W. 57th St.
    New York, N.Y. 10019

AWARDS:
Tampa Bay Art Center, prize
    awarded by Roy Slade for
    "Spontaneous Patience"
Beaux Arts, St. Petersburg

COLLECTIONS:
David A. Spinozza, N.Y.C.
Edward Kuriansky, N.Y.C.
Albert Arditi, N.Y.C.
Guy de la Rupelle, Paris
Judge Irving Cypen, Miami
Mr. & Mrs. Murray Dubbin, Miami
Millard Gamble, III, Tampa
Warren Mack, Tampa
Verlan Shirley, Tampa
Dr. Allen Trailins, S.F.
and numerous others

Bradley Arthur apprenticed for
metal sculptor Hugh Dumont in
Florida at the age of 17. His
love for sculpture grew to include
stone. He went to Southern France
and studied in the quarries with
Tony Padovano. He worked with
Japanese stone sculptor Yasuo
Mizui on one of his monuments at
the University of Nancy, France.

"THE HIGHNESS IS UNDERSTANDING
IT'S INSIDE" 12" x 24" Found Object,
Copper, Brass & Cotton NFS
© Be Art 1978 Private collection of
David A. Spinozza, N.Y.C.

ASCHER, MARY
116 Central Park South
New York, N.Y. 10019

BORN:
England

GALLERY:
Womanart Gallery
    41 West 57th Street
    New York, N.Y. 10019

EXHIBITIONS:
National Arts Club, 30 Year Retrospective, N.Y.
12 one-artist shows and numerous selected
    group shows in U.S. & abroad
50 U.S. traveling exbtns., lithograph series

AWARDS:
Huntington Hartford Fellowship
International Women's Year 75/76
C.C.N.Y., 125th Anniversary Medal
"Best of Womanart 1977," N.Y., Oils

COLLECTIONS:
WIZO, Israel, 12 Women of the Old Testament
    & Apocrypha, Oils
National Collections, Wash., D.C., Smithsonian
    Print Portfolio, 12 prints
Butler Institute of American Art
Norfolk Museum, Va.

"CORRIDORS OF POWER: Communication 2-A"
52" x 40" Oil

ATKINS, ROSALIE M.
106 Spearfish La., West
Jupiter, Florida 33458

GALLERY:
Lighthouse Gallery
Gallery Square North
Tequesta, Florida 33458

EXHIBITIONS:
"Appalachian Corridors" Exbtn.
"WV Artists on the Move," Travel. Exbt.
Allied Artists of WV Exbtns.
Exhibition 280, Huntington, WV
Natl League Am. Pen Women, Wash., D.C.
Charleston Art Gallery, WV
Tirca Carlis Gallery, Provincetown, Ma.
Provincetown Art Assoc., Ma.
Am. Drawing Biennial, Portsmouth, Va.
Soc. of the Four Arts, Palm Beach, Fla.
Lighthouse Gallery, Focus on Fla. Exbt.

AWARDS:
Allied Artists of WV Exbtns.
Exhibition 280, Huntington Galleries
Rhododendron Festival, Charleston, WV
and many others

COLLECTIONS:
WV Arts & Humanities Council
and many private collections

Rosalie Atkins studied at Mason College of
Music and Fine Arts and Morris Harvey
College. She also spent many summers at
the Provincetown Workshop and the Truro
Art Center in Massachusetts. Mrs. Atkins
works with acrylics, collage and batik,
using bold colors and designs, letting
her imagination explore an idea to create
a work of art that will both excite and
satisfy the viewer. She has had many one-
artist and invitational shows and is
listed in *Who's Who in American Art* and
Provincetown Painters, published by the
Everson Museum of Art in Syracuse, N.Y.

"THE MARKET" 1978 42" x 34" Acrylic

ATLAS-WITTKIN, LYNNE
3 Washington Square Village
New York, N.Y. 10012

BORN:
Brooklyn, N.Y., May 29, 1920

EXHIBITIONS:
One-artist shows:
Staten Island College
Tower Gallery, Southampton, N.Y.
New School for Social Research
Womanart Gallery
Jeanne Taylor Gallery
Lincoln Center
National Arts Club
National Academy of Design

AWARDS:
Womanart Gallery, First Prize-Sculpture
New School for Social Research,
Scholarship Prize-Oil Painting

COLLECTIONS:
Represented in private collections throughout
the East Coast & in London, England

Lynne Atlas-Wittkin received her art training
at the Art Students League, New York University
and the New School for Social Research.

"COUPLE" 1976–77 23" x 16" x 16" Bronze $3,500.

AUGUSTAS, ADELE U.
219 E. 32nd St.
New York, N.Y. 10016

"ARCHED FORM" 26" Stone NFS

EXHIBITIONS:
Springfield Museum of Fine Arts
New England Sculptors Assoc.
Painters & Sculptors Soc. of N.J.
Galerie Internationale, N.Y.
Avanti Galleries, N.Y.
and others, including 4
two-artist shows

AWARDS:
Sydney Taylor Memorial Prize
Esto '76, Baltimore Sculp. Prize
and others

COLLECTIONS:
Many public & private

Born in Estonia, Adele Augustas
studied art there and at the School
of Fine Arts, Boston and the
National Academy School of Fine
Arts, N.Y.

"CLOUD FORM" 1973 16½" x 15½" Alabaster NFS

AVRIN, MARC
21–6 Normandy Village
Nanuet, N.Y. 10954

GALLERIES:
Galerie Internationale
1095 Madison Ave.
New York, N.Y. 10028
The Reece Galleries, Inc.
39 W. 32nd St., N.Y., N.Y. 10001

EXHIBITIONS:
Lynn Kottler Galleries, N.Y.
Cheltenham Art Center, Pa.
Manitoba Soc. Artists, Winnipeg
Fleet Gallery, Winnipeg
Rockland Fdn. Award Show, N.Y.
Westchester Art Society, N.Y.
Union Carbide, N.Y.
Greenwich Art Barn, Ct.
W.A.S. Juried Exbtn.,
White Plains, N.Y.
Intl. Youth Council, Jerusalem

"78D" 22" x 19" x 5" Laminated Plywood POR

COLLECTIONS:
Many private in the U.S.,
Canada and Israel

Marc Avrin is a scientist, engineer
and sculptor.

"77A" 29" x 34" x 23" POR

BAILEY, BURK
109 Elaine St.
Rayne, Louisiana 70578

GALLERIES:
Burk Bailey Art Studio
901 The Boulevard
Rayne, Louisiana 70578
Bayou St. Gallery, Lafayette, La.
Tom Powers Gallery, Lafayette, La.

EXHIBITIONS:
One-artist shows in New York &
Lafayette, La.

COLLECTIONS:
Collections throughout the U.S.
& in Italy & Japan

Burk Bailey studied at the Art
Student's League in N.Y. from 1964
to 65. He holds a B.A. in Art from
USL in Lafayette, La. Using oils,
acrylics and pen and ink, the artist
also uses mixed media, such as earth
pigments tinted with pastels and
glazed with oil, depending on the
desired effect.

"THE TREE HE PLANTED" 26" x 24" Mixed Media

"THE RABBIT HUNTER" 18" x 24"
Mixed Media on Masonite POR

BAIN, EMILY JOHNSTON
834 Valley View Drive
Grand Prairie, Texas 75050

GALLERY:
834 Valley View Drive
Grand Prairie, Texas 75050

EXHIBITIONS:
Louisiana and Texas colleges
Lynn Kottler Galleries, N.Y.

COLLECTIONS:
Represented in private colls.
in La., Texas and Alabama

Emily Johnston Bain holds an
M.A. Degree from Louisiana
State University and an M.A.
from Tulane University.

"IMPROVISATION OF A WESTERN LANDSCAPE"
30" x 40" Oil $1,000.

BARLOW, BOWMAN O.
2887 Marrcrest West
Provo, Utah 84601

GALLERY:
Skylight Galleries
323 Romero N.W., #1
Albuquerque, N.M.

EXHIBITIONS:
Many natl juried including:
Springville Art Museum, Ut.
Trailside Gallery, Wyo.
New Mexico Art League

Mann-Hartford Gallery, Nev.
House of Lords, Provo, Ut.
Kimball Art Center, Ut.
Two 1-artist shows: Las
Vegas & Provo

AWARDS:
1st Place & many others

COLLECTIONS:
Numerous public & private
throughout Western U.S.

"SPRINGTIME IN NAVAJOLAND" 32" x 42" Oil $2,000.

BAINS, META W.

506 Highland Avenue
Oneonta, Alabama 35121

GALLERY:
Little House on Linden Art Center
2915 Linden Avenue
Birmingham, Alabama 35200

EXHIBITIONS:
Little House on Linden Art Center
Gadsden Museum of Art, Ala.
Gallery South, Montgomery, Ala.
Grand Hotel, Point Clear, Ala.
Lynn Kotter Gallery, N.Y.
Ligoa Duncan Gallery, N.Y.
Frank Duncan Gallery, Paris
Junior League Bldg, Birmingham, Ala.

AWARDS:
Birmingham Art Assn, 1st Prize
Ala. Watercolor Soc., Merchandise Award
Gadsden Art Assn, 3 Purchase Awards
Lauren Rogers Memorial Museum,
    Laurel, Miss., Coca Cola Purchase Award
Ala. State Fair, 1st Prize-3 years
Pensacola, Fla., 1st Prize

COLLECTIONS:
South Central Bell Telephone Co.
Coca Cola
Montclair Hospital, Birmingham, Ala.
Princeton Hospital, Birmingham, Ala.
First Alabama Bank of Birmingham
Gadsden Museum of Fine Arts, Ala.
Private collections in 19 states

"FIGS" 11½" x 15" Watercolor POR

"PARADE OF SAND CASTLES" 22½" x 30" Watercolor POR

Grace Baker's favorite medium is oil and her subject matter includes seascapes, landscapes, still life, portraits of people and animals. She prides herself on her smooth, skillful, detailed, life-like work. Experience has taught her that the finished painting is only as good as the drawing that preceded it. Therefore, perfection in this is important. Much thought and research goes into each.

"MABRY GRIST MILL" 18" x 24" Oil POR

"TOPAZ" 14" x 18" Oil Private Collection

BAKER, GRACE

1324 Richmond Road
P.O. Box 2962
Williamsburg, Va. 23185

EXHIBITIONS:

Am. Artists Professional League
  Grand National, N.Y.
Peninsula Arts Assn., Va.
Tidewater Arts Assn., Va.
Occasion for the Arts, Va.
Mariners Museum, Va.
UN Stamp Design Competition, N.Y.
Hampton Roads Coliseum, Va.
Many other natl. & regl. shows

AWARDS:

Many awards and honors

COLLECTIONS:

Mutual Savings & Loan, Va.
Chesapeake Pharmaceut. Assn., Va.
Blue Ribbon Restaurant, N.Y.
Mr. & Mrs. David Perry, Canada
Dr. Edward M. Jewusiak, Va.
Dr. A. L. Wilding, Va.
Dr. Glenn Shepard, Va.
Capt. & Mrs. Jos. Patterson, Jr., Va.
Mr. & Mrs. Chas. Manning, II, WV
Mr. & Mrs. John Machek, Jr., Va.
and many other public & private

BASKIN, LEONARD

Lurley Manor
Lurley Near Tiverton
Devon, England

BORN:

New Brunswick, N.J., Aug. 15, 1922

GALLERY:

Kennedy Galleries
20 E. 56th St.
New York, N.Y. 10022

COLLECTIONS:

Museum of Modern Art, N.Y.
Metropolitan Museum of Art, N.Y.
Brooklyn Museum
National Gallery of Art, Wash., D.C.
Fogg Museum of Art
and many others

"PURIM: ESTHER AND HAMAN" 1961
Woodcut, printed in black and yellow,
comp: 29⅞" x 13 1/16", sheet: 37¼" x 21¼"
Collection, The Museum of Modern Art, New York
Gift of the Jewish Museum

BARTLEY, HARRY H.
1212 Schindler Drive
Silver Spring, Maryland 20903

GALLERIES:
Atlantic Galleries
1055 Thomas Jefferson St., N.W.
Washington, D.C.

The Placebo
Kennebunkport, Maine

EXHIBITIONS:
Arts Club, N.Y., National Painters
in Casein Show-1974
Corcoran Gallery of Art, 16th area
exhibition, Washington, D.C.-1964

COLLECTIONS:
Represented in private collections
in the U.S. and Europe

"WINTER SNOW I" 20" x 24" Acrylic on Canvas NFS

BEARD, MARY

STUDIO:
Art Directions
5390 Briarcliff
W. Bloomfield, Mich. 48033

EXHIBITIONS:
Europe, Africa, Brazil &
throughout the U.S.

COLLECTIONS:
Detroit Renaissance Center
Kresge Eye Institute
Chrysler Corp.
Private colls. in Detroit,
Miami, N.Y., Southbend
& Sao Paulo, Brazil
and many others

"O.A. BEECH, PRESIDENT, BEECH
AIRCRAFT CO." 20" x 24" Oil POR

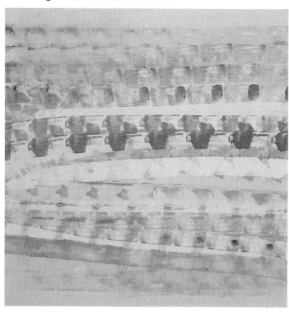

"SPEED" 1978 4' x 4' Acrylic

BERNARD, JAN DEAN
7303 Brou Lane
Houston, Texas 77074

GALLERIES:
Azim Studios
422 South Oliver
Wichita, Kansas

J. Miller
1929 North Blvd.
Houston, Texas

EXHIBITIONS:
Numerous shows

COLLECTIONS:
Private collections
throughout the U.S.

BLAYLOCK, CHARLES G.
% Artco, Incorporated
Rt. 2 - Box 109 Cuba Road
Long Grove, Illinois 60047

EXHIBITIONS:
Many national and regional
group & one-artist shows

COLLECTIONS:
Represented in many public &
private collections across U.S.

"KWAHU - Eagle Kachina" 12" x 16" Acrylic on Masonite POR

"KOYEMSI - Mudhead Kachna;
KOSHARI PALYAK YAMU - Hano Clown Kachina"
12" x 16" Acrylic on Masonite POR

BETHELL, ELOISE

P.O. Box 4202
Wilmington, N.C. 28406

EXHIBITIONS:
Polyforum Cultural
Siqueiros, Mexico
Museo Nacional de Bellas
Artes, Mexico
One-artist shows:
U.S., France, Canada,
Lebanon & Mexico

AWARDS:
Prix de Paris
and many others

COLLECTIONS:
Gallery Chapultepec, Mex.
and many others

Eloise Bethell has done
several special editions,
including pen and ink drawings
for *Ballet de Monte Carlo* and
a soon-to-be-released *Mexico —
A Landscape in People.*

"ATTIC CORNER" 17½" x 19½" Watercolor POR

BJØRNTWEDT, JENE I.

3134 Starboard Dr.
Annapolis, Maryland 21403

GALLERY:
Gallery-One II, Main St.
Annapolis, Md. 21401

EXHIBITIONS:
Annapolis & Baltimore, Md.
Washington, D.C. area
Tombstone & Phoenix, Ariz.

COLLECTIONS:
Cochise Apache Museum, AZ

"CIYE NIÑO COCHISE TIMES REMEMBERED"
24" x 30" Oil on Linen Canvas NFS

"DOUBLE, DOUBLE" 12' x 4' Concrete & Steel
Collection, Sam Houston State Univ.
©1978, Michael F. Boles

BOLES, MICHAEL F.

365 24th, S.E.
Paris, Texas 75460

GALLERY:
Kreativate
1014 Santa Fe
Corpus Christi, Tx 78404

EXHIBITIONS:
Dimension Houston XI
Arkansas Art Center
One Seguin Center, Tx.
McNamara-Oconnor,
Victoria, Texas
and numerous others

AWARDS:
Del Mar Natl, Corpus
Christi, Purchase Award
Texas Fine Arts Citation,
Best of Show
and other awards

COLLECTIONS:
Timewealth Corp.,
Houston, Texas
Numerous private colls.

Model for "DERVISH" 6½" x 5½"
Bronze POR ©1978, Michael F. Boles

Michael Boles received a Master
of Fine Arts in sculpture from
Sam Houston State University, and
has done independent study in
Europe and Mexico. He prefers
working in bronze, concrete,
steel, wood and stone.

BOGART, Sr. EVELYN

2131 W. Third St.
Los Angeles, Calif. 90057

GALLERIES:
Eugene Gallery
  262 S. Lake St.
  Los Angeles, Ca. 90057
Studio San Damiano
  Cardinal Stritch College
  Milwaukee, Wisconsin
Natl League Am. Pen Women
Intl Artists Assoc.

EXHIBITIONS:
N. Shore Country Club, Milw.
Watts, Milw., 1-artist shows
Milwaukee Athletic Club
and many others

AWARDS:
N. Shore Country Club, 3
St. Mary's Art Fair, 2
Milw. League of Artists, 3
and many others

COLLECTIONS:
Many public & private

"CURTIN CHURCH, PA." Oil NFS

BOSSERT, EDYTHE HOY

Old Beech Creek Road
Beech Creek, Pa. 16822

GALLERIES:
Millbrook Art Gallery
  Mill Hall, Pa. 17751
Farm House, Lock Haven, Pa.

EXHIBITIONS:
Natl. Academy Galleries,
  Natl. Assn. Women Artists

Lock Haven State College
Ross Library, Lock Haven
Ogunquit, Maine
Terry Art Institute, Fla.
Bucknell University, Pa.
Pa. House of Repres.

COLLECTIONS:
School & public libraries
Many public & private

"RED FLOWER" 18" x 24" Collage on Masonite POR

"DETERMINATION" 18" x 24" Charcoal POR

BROOKS, DARLENE

530 E. 4th Place
Mesa, Arizona 85203

EXHIBITIONS:
Arizona State Fair
Mesa Gold Cup Shows
Fine Arts Shows

AWARDS:
Best of Shows, Purchase
  Awards and numerous other
  ribbons & awards

COLLECTIONS:
Private collections in
  U.S., Canada & England

"REV. DR. SEYMOUR ST. JOHN, HEADMASTER, THE CHOATE SCHOOL, WALLINGFORD, CT." 36" x 48" Oil
©Robert G. Bowen, Jr. 1965

BROWN, JAMES
117–54 219th St.
Cambria Heights, N.Y. 11411

"DANAKIL" 38" x 27" Oil POR

GALLERY:
Roads Galleries
400 E. 57th St., N.Y., N.Y. 10022

EXHIBITIONS:
One-Artist shows:
Corpus Christi Museum, Texas
American Intl. Coll., Mass.
Windermere Art Gallery, Fla.
Panoras Art Gallery, N.Y.
Atlantic City Art Center, N.J.
Lynn Kottler Gallery, N.Y.
Over 40 exbtns. since 1974

AWARDS:
Numerous awards in juried shows

COLLECTIONS:
N.Y.C. Public Schools
Corpus Christi Museum
Yale University
Over 100 private collections
including singer Donna Summer

"HARLEM STREET SCENE" 28" x 40" Oil POR

BROWN, VIRGINIA BENSON
611 Carner Ct., E.
Richland, Washington 99352

GALLERY:
Mushroom Gallery
714 Sprague
Spokane, Washington

EXHIBITIONS:
Cheney Cowles Museum, 29th Annual
National Art Auction, Wash., D.C.,
Sponsored by American Kidney Fdn.
Mushroom Gallery, Spokane, Wash.,
2-artist show

AWARDS:
Artists of Central Wash. Exhibit,
20th Annual, Honorable Mention

COLLECTIONS:
Represented in numerous public
and private collections

The artist enjoys the use of nature as
a starting point to depart into a fantasy
world of imaginative dimensions.

She is listed in the Registry of Northwest
Artists at the Henry Gallery, University
of Washington.

"BLOSSOM IMAGERY #4" 1978 30" x 40"
Oil & Gold Leaf $700.

BROWN, DON LELAND
Route 1, Box 957
McHenry, Illinois 60050

GALLERIES:
Stockbridge Gallery
   209 W. Jackson Blvd.
   Chicago, Ill. 60606
Davis Studios
   86 Main Ave.
   Clinton, Iowa 52732

EXHIBITIONS:
One-artist & multi-artist
   shows in 9 states and
   Washington, D.C.

AWARDS:
3 Awards of Excellence
4 First Place Awards
3 Purchase Awards

COLLECTIONS:
National Archives, Wash., DC
Decision Consultants, Detroit
Natl Cash Register, Detroit
Employer's Mutual Insurance,
   Wausau, Wisc.
Marathon Cnty, Wausau, Wisc.

"ANGRY MAN"
18" x 24"
Serigraph $90.

"THE LATCH" 28" x 34" Watercolor POR

BUTLER, GERRI H.
P.O. Box 11360
Chicago, Illinois 60611

GALLERIES:
Art Institute of Chicago
Artists Guild of Chicago
Gehebu-AK, Chicago

EXHIBITIONS:
Many 1-artist & group

AWARDS:
Huntington Hartford Grant
Water Tower Competition
Illinois State Fairs
Many prizes & commissions

COLLECTIONS:
Numerous public & private

BULLOCK, TIMOTHY ASA
P.O. Box 4243
Long Beach, California 90804

"THE LAMB OF CHRIST" 1970, Private coll.
14" x 18" India Ink on Illustration Board
Represents presence of an Almighty Force.

"THE DREAMER" 1976 24" x 36" Oil on Canvas
Private collection of Mrs. Anita Legvolt, Irvine, Ca.
Represents imagination of man tying together multiple planes of life.

Born on August 21, 1951 in Lynchburg, Virginia, Timothy Asa Bullock studied stage lighting and design at Long Beach City College and studied calligraphy with Maurice B. Nugent for four years until his death in 1973. A member of the Long Beach Art Association, Mr. Bullock's media include oil, India ink, watercolor, acrylic, charcoal and pastel chalks. He works in surrealism, realism and does graphic illustrations. The artworks shown are surrealistic studies in depth.

BROWNING, DIXIE B.

5316 Robin Hood Road
Winston-Salem, N.C. 27106

GALLERIES:

Art Gallery Originals
  120 Reynolda Village
  Winston-Salem, N.C.
Island Gallery, Manteo, N.C.
McNeal Gallery
  1626 East Blvd., Charlotte, N.C.

EXHIBITIONS:

Irene Leache Biennial, Norfolk, Va.
Watercolor Soc. of N.C.
Gallery of Contemporary Art,
  Winston-Salem, N.C.
Associated Artists of N.C.
Contemporary Graphic Artists,
  traveling shows
more than 2 dozen group & one-artist

AWARDS:

Associated Artists of N.C.,
  Best in Show-1971
Winston-Salem Gallery of Fine Art,
  Purchase Prize
Associated Artists of Winston-Salem,
  First Prize-1972, 1975
Southport Fine Arts Festival,
  First in Watercolor-1967, 1971;
  First in Oils-1968
and many other area & regl. awards

COLLECTIONS:

U.S. Coast Guard Museum, Permanent
  Collection, New London, Ct.
Rachel Maxwell Moore Art Foundation,
  Greenville Art Center, N.C.
R.J. Reynolds World Headquarters
Statesville Museum, N.C.
Lowenstein Collection
Southport Municipal Collection, N.C.
Mary Reynolds Babcock Foundation
Integon Corporation
Wachovia Bank & Trust Co.
and others

Dixie Browning is the first president
of the Watercolor Society of N.C. and a
past vice president of the Associated
Artists of Winston-Salem, N.C. She
co-founded and is on the board of
directors of Art Gallery Originals in
Winston-Salem. An illustrator and the
author of five novels written under
the penname of Zoe Dozier, Ms. Browning
is listed in *Who's Who in American Art*
and *World Who's Who of Women*.

"MARSHSCAPE FOR ZOE" 16" x 20" Watercolor
Collection of Mrs. J. Grisham, Chapel Hill, N.C.

BUZZO, MARGE
Marge Buzzo Studio
21500 Wyandotte St., #101
Canoga Park, Calif. 91303

4620 Santa Lucia Dr.
Woodland Hills, Calif. 9136

GALLERIES:
Shirley Meyers
1951 S. Coast Hwy.
Laguna Bch, Calif. 9265
Harry Lauter Art Gallery
Ojai, Calif. 93023

EXHIBITIONS:
Burbank Public Libr., Ca.
Independence Bank, Ca.
Channel 28, Hollywood, Ca.
Descanso Gardens, L.A.

AWARDS:
1st Place & many others

COLLECTIONS:
Burbank Public Library
Many private throughout U.S.

"SUMMER PASTIME" 22" x 28" Mixed Media POR

CARDOSO, ANTHONY A.
3208 Nassau Street
Tampa, Florida 33607

GALLERIES:
Warren Gallery
2710 MacDill Ave.
Tampa, Fla. 33609
Ligoa Duncan, N.Y.

EXHIBITIONS:
Paris International
N.Y. International

Salon of 50 States, N.Y.
Latham Fdn. International
Smithsonian, Wash., D.C.

AWARDS:
"Prix de Paris" Intl.
Lathan Fdn. International
and others

COLLECTIONS:
Over 700 public & private

"THE CLOWN" 24" x 30" Acrylic $500.

CARD, ROYDEN
991 S. Geneva Rd.
Orem, Utah 84057

GALLERY:
Annex Gallery
604 College Ave.
Santa Rose, Calif.

BORN:
Alberta, Canada; 1952

EXHIBITIONS:
Utah Museum of Fine Arts,
All Utah Show-1978

AWARDS:
All Utah Show,
Purchase Award-1978

COLLECTIONS:
Utah Arts Council

"MOUNTAINS II" 9½" x 14" Woodcut $50. (Unframed)

"JENNI'S TABLE" 10½" x 13" Woodcut $50. (Unframed)

"SWIMMING" 72" x 96" Oil on Leather & Canvas

CAICED, JAIMME D.
105–48 63rd Road
Forest Hills, N.Y. 11375

EXHIBITIONS:
  10 one-artist & 56 group shows

AWARDS:
  25 prizes throughout the U.S.,
  Canada, S. America & Europe

Jaimme D. Caiced's new and original technique consists of achieving a three-dimensional effect on leather, wood and canvas.

COLLECTIONS:
  The White House, portraits of
    Presidents John F. Kennedy
    and Lyndon B. Johnson
  Mrs. Jacqueline Kennedy
  Cardinal Spellman
  Pope John XXIII
  Vatican Collection
  Mr. Edward Goldberg
  Sen. Sheldon Farber
  Public & private collections in the
    U.S., Canada, S. America & Europe

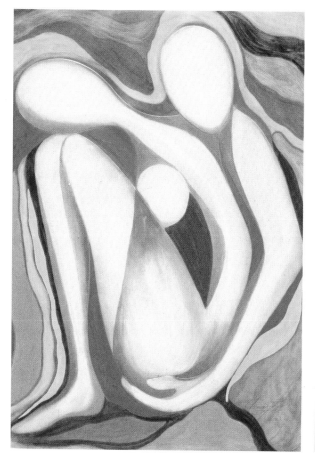

"TWINS" 36" x 48" Oil

"NEW YORK NIGHTS" 65" x 86" Oil on Leather & Canvas

CARLSON, VINCENT J.
3225 Loretto Road
Jacksonville, Florida 32217

BORN:
Jamestown, N.Y., Nov. 12, 1916

EXHIBITIONS:
Pocono Pines, Pocono Mts., Pa.
Great Barrington, Mass. Art Exbt.

COLLECTIONS:
Private collections in 7 states

"THE RETREAT" 24" x 30" Oil POR

CASE, JOANNE
5268 Parejo Drive
Santa Barbara, Calif. 93111

GALLERIES:
Bradley Gallery,
  Santa Barbara
Ira Roberts Publishers,
  Beverly Hills
Jack O'Grady, Chicago

EXHIBITIONS:
Jack O'Grady Gallery,
  Chicago

COLLECTIONS:
Many private across U.S.

"FAMILY FARM" 30" x 40" Acrylic POR

CASE, JOHN W.
2300 Lincoln Avenue
Fort Worth, Texas 76106

BORN:
Ft. Worth, Tex., Aug. 24, 1947

EXHIBITIONS:
Lynn Kottler Galleries, N.Y.,
  3-artist show, 1976
Ligoa Duncan Gallery, Salon
  of the 50 States, N.Y., 1977
Ligoa Duncan Gallery, Salon
  of the 50 States, N.Y., 1978

"VISION" 16" x 20" Oil on Canvas $750.

CHIVIAN, GEORGIA
6 Westgate Road
Livingston, N.J. 07039

AGENT:
Albert Saifer
115 E. 9th, N.Y., N.Y. 10003

"THE LOVERS" Pink Alabaster 15" x 24" $1,200.

CHAGALL, MARC
Les Collines
Vence
Alpes Maritimes, France

"THE STORY OF EXODUS" New York-Paris. Leon Amiel. 1966
One of twenty-four color lithographs, comp (irreg.): 18" x 13¼"
Collection, The Museum of Modern Art, New York
Gift of Mr. Lester Avnet

CHANEY, RUFFIN A.
640 River Side Drive
New York, N.Y. 10031

Ruffin Chaney was born in Philadelphia in 1952. His development as an artist in matchwork sculpture began at the age of twelve. He was attending Swarthmore Elementary School when he completed his first artistic sculpture with matches. His parents encouraged him in his endeavors, but knew of no way of helping him exploit his talents,. Since then, he has completed many art pieces, which have been shown privately. He has had little in the way of professional art training, learning through his exposure to other artists and art media.

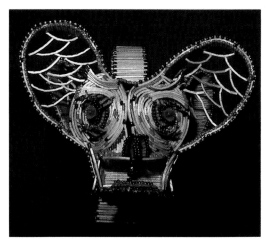

"USIRFURE"

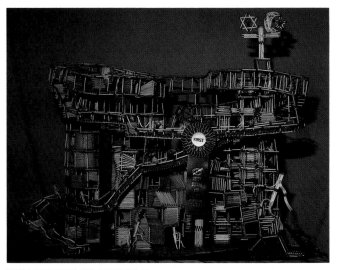

"STAIRSTEPS TO HEAVEN"

An engaging look at "Stairsteps to Heaven" gives the viewer more insight into how profound an artistic statement Mr. Chaney makes with his art. His "Usirfure," a marvelously constructed sculptured head, literally leers at the viewer. It seems to dare you not to see your inner-self reflexed in its intricacy and overpowering beauty.

Other than exhibiting privately, Mr. Chaney has also exhibited publicly in Greenwich Village, N.Y., Cable TV, and recently won first prize at the arts and crafts fair at Ghetty Square Park, Yonkers, N.Y., an achievement of the highest order.

CHESHIRE, RUTH
774 Larkfield Road
East Northport, N.Y. 11731

GALLERY:
Cheshire Studio Gallery
774 Larkfield Road
East Northport, N.Y. 11731

EXHIBITIONS:
Heckscher Museum, Huntington, NY
European-American Bank,
  Elwood, N.Y., 1-artist

Adelphi Univ., Garden City
Huntington, N.Y., two
  1-artist shows
American Assoc. of Univ.
  Women, N.Y.
Kottler Galleries, N.Y.

COLLECTIONS:
Public & private throughout
  the U.S.

"BARN INTERIOR" 13" x 15" Pen & Ink POR

"THE ALBUM" 24" x 36" Oil POR

CHUA HU

℅ Ligoa Duncan "Arts"
22 E. 72nd Street
New York, N.Y. 10021

822 Benavides Street
Binondo, Manila, Philippines

"GREAT WALL OF CHINA" 33" x 55"

GALLERIES:
 Galeries Raymond Duncan
 31 rue de Seine, Paris, France

 Ligoa Duncan Gallery
 22 E. 72nd Street
 New York, N.Y. 10021

EXHIBITIONS:
 One-artist shows:
  Ligoa Duncan, N.Y.-1977
  Galeries Raymond Duncan,
   Paris-1976 & 78
  Leland Art Gallery, Taiwan
  City Exbtn Hall, Hong Kong
  Art Assn of the Philippines
 Group shows:
  Chinese Artists from Manila,
   Formosa-1971
  10-artists show-tour to Taipei
  8-artists show-tour to Taipei
   & Taichun, Taiwan-1959
  Salon des Surindependants,
   Musee du Luxembourg, Paris-1978
  Academie Internationale de
   Lutece, Paris-1978

AWARDS:
 Art Assn of the Philippines,
  11th Annual Compet., 1st Prize
 Several awards in Europe & the
  Dominican Republic-1977–78

"SILVERY WATERFALL" 33" x 55" Oil $1,500.

"ANCIENT TEMPLE OF CHINA" 33" x 55"

Chua Hu, born in Chin-Kang, China in 1929, migrated to the Philippines in 1939 and is now a permanent resident. He studied Chinese painting there under Yang Keng Tong, life painting under Prof. Victorio Edades at the University of Santo Tomas, and has a BFA degree from Malayan Colleges, Manila. Chua Hu was president of the Philippine-Chinese Artists League in 1959 and published his first art book, "Chua Hu Oil Painting" in 1971.

From "JOURNAL DE L'AMATEUR D'ART"—May, 1978

"For this big Parisian exposition, Chua Hu is understood as the "Chinese Artist from Manila." The fact is, he was born in China in 1929 but in 1938, emigrated to the Philippines where he now resides. It is his second exposition in Paris at Galeries Raymond Duncan, but he has, likewise, exhibited at Salon des Surindependants.

"Since last year, Chua Hu has been affirming a stronger personality in an authentic painting, with dominant blue which he sometimes extends, to a certain limit, to black. In such manner, he achieves contrasts and a profundity, which is not the least charm of his painting, that is essentially of atmosphere. An impression of fluidity is released from the collection of this synthesis between the East and the West. When, having returned to Manila, he paints Paris, it is evidently a painting of souvenirs, but more so, a painting of impressions; the most famous monuments of the capitol are found there, but, one could say, they are treated in synthesis and detach themselves in a thick bluish mist. Paris seems to emerge from the sea over which the painter flies at the time of his travels, the sea where men are found in a boat, being his symbol of identity: sea-fronts, bridges equally inspire him. Also, his impressions continually revolve around structured elements.

"Before coming to France for a short stay at the time of his expositions, Chua Hu had exhibited in Formosa with the Artists from Manila, in New York at the Ligoa Duncan Gallery, in Taiwan and in Hong Kong.

"Chua Hu is most comfortable in grand sizes. He paints them in such a way that our gaze penetrates in the canvas of a vast, silent landscape as "After the Rain" close to "Manila Harbor." We rock gently to the same rhythm as the Sampans, we are taken by the atmosphere of these strange bluish nights. The limit of abstraction here takes its meaning as the nature itself, when we guess what we do not see, when the center of interest is such that it blurs out the shapes, when only a part of the whole is perceived, when we feel nothing but the effect of light, a feeling of air and of space.

"The present exposition deservingly titled, "Symphony in Blue" is orchestrated by the unity of canvasses, similar to each other and yet so strongly different from one another as to release an impression of serenity, inviting one to a quiet contemplation, when everything is in one harmony, the artist especially searching for unity without variations as the theme of his compositions."

CHUA HU

From "VISION SUR LES ARTS"—April, 1978

"The works of Chua Hu, born from his concentration and profound mastery, are suitable poetic evocations. Chua Hu gives way to his impulses—this vibrant sonority is omnipresent even when it is checked. This artist, born in China, lives only for his painting. Avoiding the strict realistic image, he has found his really personal expression.

"It is thanks to a powerful inner necessity, inspired by Zen meditation, that he was led to create his own universe. Chua Hu feels especially at ease with large paintings matching the effervescent feelings within himself. The artist feels akin to Cezanne, Madrian for the love of a scientifically structured construction, and to Monet for the grievering search for air and light.

"Chua Hu's style is concise, determined, and yet supple and ethereal. Chua Hu is above all a poet, who likes to give way to calm and vigilant dreams!

"He uses a soothing kind of blue which vibrates with white in secret chords while creating supple rhythms.

"With Chua Hu, colors carry us into a spiritualized world liberated from any material heaviness. As to his style, close to cubism, it is an approach to purism."

—Hermance Molina

"PARIS—MEMORY"

CIVALE, BIAGIO
311 Lee Avenue
Yonkers, N.Y. 10705

GALLERIES:
Over 60 worldwide

EXHIBITIONS:
More than 100 worldwide

COLLECTIONS:
Various museums
Public & private
collections worldwide

"MEXICAN BOY SLEEPING OUTDOORS" 1974 Serigraph

"CROWN" 22" x 30" Intaglio $80.

CORDUA, HARNEY
4340 Altamirano Way
San Diego, Calif. 92103

EXHIBITIONS:
Fine Arts Gall, San Diego
San Diego Community Arts
Gallery, All Media Show

Grad. School for Urban
Resources & Social
Policy
San Diego Art Institute

COLLECTIONS:
Private colls. in Calif.

"MY TOTEM"
Stained Glass
& Steel

CRAWFORD, RUTH A.
304 Rio Vista Place
Santa Fe, N.M. 87501

BORN:
Texas

GALLERIES:
Kachina Gallery,
Santa Fe, N.M. 87501
Triangle Home Cntr Gallery,
Clovis, N.M. 88101

EXHIBITIONS:
Southwest Arts & Crafts,
Albuquerque, N.M.
Western Art, San Antonio, Tex
Best of the Southwest,
Amarillo, Texas
Home Show, Houston, Texas
Other natl & regl shows

COSSOCK, EVA
4511 E. 7th St.
Tucson, Arizona 85711

GALLERY:
Artist's Studio
4511 E. 7th St.
Tucson, Arizona 85711

EXHIBITIONS:
Tucson Museum of Art
Kentucky Art Guild Train

Phoenix Art Museum
R.I. School of Design
and other 1-artist & group
regl. & natl. shows

AWARDS:
Copper Sculp. Show, Ariz.
R.I. School of Design
and others

COLLECTIONS:
Many private & public

"TAOS INDIAN" 14" x 18" Oil $350.

CONESA, MIGUEL A.

GALLERIES:
The M. Osuna Gallery
901 Rosedale Ave., S.E.
Atlanta, Georgia 30312
Lynn Kottler Galleries, N.Y.
Galleria Hispania, Ponce, P.R.
and many others

EXHIBITIONS:
Ligoa Duncan Gallery, N.Y.
High Museum, Atlanta, Ga.
UNESCO, Cultural Affairs, P.R.
Royal Bank of Canada, P.R.
Over 50 group & 16 artist shows

COLLECTIONS:
Munich Museum, Germany
High Museum, Atlanta, Ga.
Ponce Art Museum, P.R.
Augusta Richmond Museum, Ga.
McDuffie Collection, Thomson, Ga.
and many other public & private
collections worldwide

"THERE WAS A MAN NAMED
JOHN. . .
WHO DIED OF OLD AGE,
NO ONE CAME TO HIS FUNERAL,
NO ONE NEITHER LOVED,
                    KNEW OR
UNDERSTOOD HIM.
STRANGE HANDS BRING
HIM FLOWERS NOW AND THEN.
NO FLOWER EVER FADES
AT HIS GRAVE,
NOT EVEN IN WINTER. . ."

1977–78 36" x 48" Acrylic, modeling
paste, sand, tissue paper on canvas
$25,000.

"PORTRAIT OF A VISITOR
FROM ANOTHER GALAXY. . ."
18" x 24" Acrylic, tissue paper,
modeling paste $5,000.

AWARDS:
Catholic Univ., Ponce, P.R.,
Best of Show
Art Festival, Thomson, Ga.,
Best of Show
and many others

"PRISONER OF SELF" 1976 24" x 36"
Acrylic, modeling paste, tissue paper on canvas NFS

"THE COSMOS. . . THE SCIENTIST" 1976–77 31" x 40"
Acrylic & modeling paste $12,000.

CULLNAN, SHARON M.
Rt. 5, 127th Street
Lemont, Illinois 60439

EXHIBITIONS:
Field Museum, Chicago
Prudential Bldg., Chicago
Hauserman Orchid

Joliet Library,
 One-artist show
Chicago Public Library

AWARDS:
 Am. Orchid Soc. Special
 LAFG Special Award

COLLECTIONS:
 Numerous in U.S. & Europe

"LIGHTS, CAMERA, ACTION" 12" x 16"
Oil $90.

CURTIS, LOIS
Box 854
Grants, New Mexico 87020

"HASN'T WALKED" 4" x 6½" Bronze Edition of 12 $495.

"CAJUN BAYOU" 16" x 20" Oil $200.

DABBS, MIRIAM
℅ Ligoa Duncan Gallery
22 East 72nd Street
New York, N.Y. 10021

321 Maple
Clarksdale, Miss. 38614

EXHIBITIONS:
1-artist shows in N.Y.;

Galeries Raymond Duncan,
 Paris, & in the South
Salon des Surindependants

AWARDS:
 Raymond Duncan, Prix de
 Paris, 4 times
 Intl. Art Festival, Paris

COLLECTIONS:
 Many collections

DAIGLE, ROGER R.
2423 W. Morton
Denison, Texas 75020

EXHIBITIONS:
 Denison Public Library,
 1-artist show-1978

AWARDS:
 DACS Art Exhibit, Best of
 Show (2 consec. yrs.) &
 2nd Place, Acrylics

COLLECTIONS:
 Represented in private
 throughout the U.S.

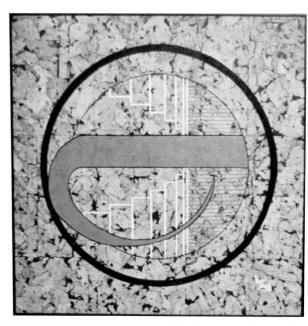

"GEOMETRIC PUEBLO" 20" x 20" Acrylic on Cork POR

DALI, SALVADOR

Hotel St. Regis
New York, N.Y. 10022

BORN:
Figueras, Spain, May 11, 1904

EXHIBITIONS:
Julien Levy Gallery, N.Y.
Arts Club, Chicago
Dalzell Hatfield Galleries, L.A.
Museum of Modern Art, N.Y.
Knoedler Gallery, N.Y.
and many others

"THE PERSISTENCE OF MEMORY (PERSISTANCE DE LA
MEMOIRE)" 1931 Oil on Canvas 9½" x 13"
Collection, The Museum of Modern Art, New York
Given anonymously

DAVIS-BANKS, PHYLLIS EILEEN

5714 College Drive
Anchorage, Alaska 99504

GALLERIES:
The Gallery, 817 W. 7th Ave.
Anchorage, Alaska 99501
David's Casa de Art, N.M.

EXHIBITIONS:
One-artist shows:
Contemporary Portraits,
Women of the Bible
American Soc. of Artists,
Interpreting Gibran

AWARDS:
Alaska Watercolor Society,
Purchase Award

COLLECTIONS:
Anchorage Fine Arts Museum
Many private collections

Ms. Davis-Banks is listed in
Who's Who in the West-1978.

"EARTH EXHALATION" 24" x 30" Watercolor $175.

DANILA

P.O. Box 503
Southern Pines, N.C. 28387

Instituto d'Arte di Firenze
Ringling School of Art

EXHIBITIONS:
SEIFAS, Royal Exchange, London
Primer Salon, Panama City, R.P.
Italian Artists in U.S.A.
Italian Cultural Center
Red Mile Club, Lexington, Ky.

AWARDS:
Wildlife Fed. Show, Raleigh, N.C.,
First Prize-1974 & 1977
I-40 Art Expo, Winslow, Ariz.,
1st Prize, Animal Painting
Many other 1st & Purchase Prizes

COLLECTIONS:
Ft. Leavenworth Museum, Kansas
Museum of Arts & Science, N.C.
Many private in U.S. & abroad

"CAROLINA THOROUGHBREDS" 32" x 40" Conte & Ink

"BEFORE THE RACE" 18" x 30" Watercolor

Da PRATO, JOHN
61 Puffer Lane
Sudbury, Mass. 01776

BORN:
Viareggio, Italy;
Sept. 20, 1947

A graduate of Boston University, John Da Prato's style comprises "non-objective" art, sometimes dealing with compositions having clean, straight lines, sometimes delving into the area of freer abstraction. Non-objective art features a lack of objects found in real life. An innovator, his art is a departure from the world as we perceive it.

Photographs by
Barry Marc Real

"DANCERS" 24" x 36" Mixed Media on Paper NFS

"MOONLIGHT" 24" x 30"
Acrylic on Canvas $250.

DeBAUN, BARRY
Trail Motel, Rt. 28
Boiceville, N.Y. 12412

BORN:
Brooklyn, N.Y., Oct. 17, 1956

GALLERY:
The DeBaun Gallery
Trail Motel, Rt. 28
Boiceville, N.Y. 12412

EXHIBITIONS:
One-artist shows:
Bowery Bank, Main Branch
N.Y.-1978
Inter-County Savings Bank,
New Paltz, N.Y.-1978
Roundout National Bank,
Kingston, N.Y.-1977
Catskill House,
Woodstock, N.Y.-1977
Springfield Museum of Fine
Arts, Mass., Contemporary
Realism Show-1977
Berkshire Museum, Mass.,
Spring Show-1975
Albany Institute of History &
Art, N.Y., Mohawk-Hudson
Regional Show-1975

AWARDS:
American Artist First National
Art Competition,
Semi-finalist
Hunter Mt., N.Y. Art Show,
Best in Show-1978

COLLECTIONS:
Over 60 private collections
throughout the U.S.

"GOLDEN LIGHT" 17½" x 26½" Watercolor POR

"SOLAR SYSTEM EXIT"   48" x 72" Oil on Belgium Linen POR

De CRESCENZO, DOMINIC

% Ligoa Duncan Gallery
22 East 72nd Street
New York, N.Y. 10021

BORN:
New York City, 1948

EXHIBITIONS:
Ligoa Duncan Gallery, N.Y.,
   Salon of the 50 States
Raymond Duncan Galeries,
   Paris-Dec., 1976
Ligoa Duncan Gallery,
   1-artist show-Oct., 1977
Surindependants Luxembourg
   Museum, Paris-1977 & 78
Many group shows in U.S.

AWARDS:
Prix de Paris-1977

COLLECTIONS:
Many private collections

"SPACE PROBES ARE A MUST"
30" x 30" Oil on Linen POR

"POINT OF ENTRY" 36" x 48" Oil on Masonite POR

From PARK EAST NEWS,
Hulda G. Lawrence, Editor:
"A fascinating exhibition of oil
paintings in a surrealistic
manner by Dominic De Crescenzo
was seen at the Ligoa Duncan
Gallery October 15. Two splendid
works, 'Space Probes are a Must'
and 'Exploration Through
Heritage' captured the real
feeling of outer space with its
infinite distances and multitudes
of stars. In both paintings,
space vehicles moved in the
vastness of the heavens. 'Point
of Entry' was used as the focus
of this show and it was a fine
example of this artist's understanding of distance relation-
ships and the clarity of color.
We glimpsed infinity through an
oval opening and were drawn
within this very appealing scene.
To catch the breadth of this
artist's paintings, they must
be seen."

Above color paintings photographed by Mr. Eriberto Santiago.

"WOMAN, XI" 1961 29" x 22⅜"
Oil & Pastel on paper mounted on canvas
The Sidney & Harriet Janis Collection
Gift to The Museum of Modern Art, New York

de KOONING, WILLEM
Woodbine Drive
The Springs
East Hampton, N.Y. 11973

BORN:
Rotterdam, Holland

EXHIBITIONS:
Many one-artist & group shows

COLLECTIONS:
Art Institute of Chicago
Metropolitan Museum of Art, N.Y.
Museum of Modern Art, N.Y.
Whitney Museum of Am. Art, N.Y.
and many others

DeVITO, TERESA M.
417 Newton Street
Fairmont, W. Va. 26554

GALLERY:
Lynn Kottler
3 E. 65th, N.Y., N.Y. 10021

EXHIBITIONS:
Charleston-Festival
Rhododendron
Clarksburg Show

Elkins Festival
Exbt 60, Morgantown
Pittsburgh Watercolor Soc.
Palace Grassi, Venice
Immaculate Conception Church,
Fairmont, W. Va.

AWARDS:
Many awards

COLLECTIONS:
Many private collections

"EARTH I" 20" x 28"
Acrylic POR

DOEBRICH, LEE G.
℅ Mary Joyce
622 Hope St.
Providence, R.I. 02906

GALLERY:
Lenore Gray Gallery
15 Meeting St.
Providence, R.I.

"PROGRESSION, PART 1" 12" x 24" Silk Screen
Limited Ed. POR

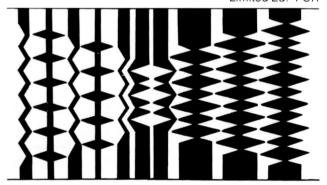

"IS THIS SEAT TAKEN?" 1978. 36" x 48" Acrylic

DORRIS, PARKY
Route 4
Cleveland, Ga. 30528

BORN:
Athens, Tn, April 7, 1951

GALLERIES:
Appalachian Gallery
Box 274
Young Harris, Ga. 30582
Stilwind Graphics, Box 230
Helen, Ga. 30545

EXHIBITIONS:
Atlanta Mem. Arts Center
Peidmont Arts Festival
Roswell Arts Festival
Toccoa-Stevens Art Fest.
2-artist show, Atlanta

COMMISSIONS:
Matterhorn Restaurant,
Helen, Georgia
River House Restaurant,
Tallulah Falls, Georgia

"PARIS SMILES" 1976 Etching with sugarlift ground and woodblock,
printed in black, brilliant blue, dark gray, deep yellow green,
and brown orange, plate: 23¾" x 20", sheet: 35⅞" x 24⅞".
Collection, The Museum of Modern Art, New York
Gift of the artist and Aldo Crommelynck.

DINE, JIM
℅ The Pace Gallery
32 E. 57th St.
New York, N.Y.

BORN:
Cincinnati, Ohio, June 16, 1935

EXHIBITIONS:
Pace Galleries, N.Y.
Martha Jackson Gallery, N.Y.
Janis Gallery, N.Y.
Marlborough Gallery, N.Y.
Museum of Modern Art, N.Y
Whitney Museum of Am. Art, N.Y.
One-artist shows throughout the world

COLLECTIONS:
Museum of Modern Art, N.Y.
Tate Gallery, London
Stedelijk Museum, Holland
Whitney Museum of Am. Art, N.Y.
Albright-Knox Art Gallery, Buffalo
and many others

DUNCAN, LIGOA

℅ Ligoa Duncan "Arts"
22 East 72nd Street
New York, N.Y. 10021

31 rue de Seine
Paris 75006 France

EXHIBITIONS:
Ligoa Duncan Gallery, N.Y.
Great Neck Community Center, N.Y.
Chatauqua Arts Festival, N.Y.
Tucson Art Center, Arizona
Salon Francais, Tucson, Arizona
Salon l'Image Festival Intl d'Art
  Contemporain, Allonnes, France
Salon des Artiste Francais, Grand
  Palais des Champs Elysees, Paris,
  1st photographer to participate, by
  invitation of Henri Heraut, 1977–78
Salon des Surindependants, Musée du
  Luxembourg, Paris-1977, 78, 1st
  photographer
"La Bretagne" Salon-Expo at Tour
  Montparnasse, Paris
Artistes USA Prix de Paris,
  Galeries Raymond Duncan, Paris
Ukrainian Institute of America, N.Y.
  In connection with the centenaries
  of Raymond & Isadora Duncan
"Semaine Memoriale," Paris-1978
Museum of the Theatre, Salonika & Athens
Academie Internationale de Lutece-1978

Ligoa Duncan was born in Paris
under the aegis of the Akademia
Raymond Duncan. She is the
daughter of Raymond Duncan and
follows the creative traditions of
the Duncan family, among whose
members are: Isadora, Augustine,
Elizabeth and Raymond. Ligoa
Duncan is not only a
photographer, but also an
art-weaver, a singer expressing the
mood of many lands, an

"AIA, RAYMOND, LIGOA IN THE ALPS"
16" x 20" Sykronokrome ©1977 $150.

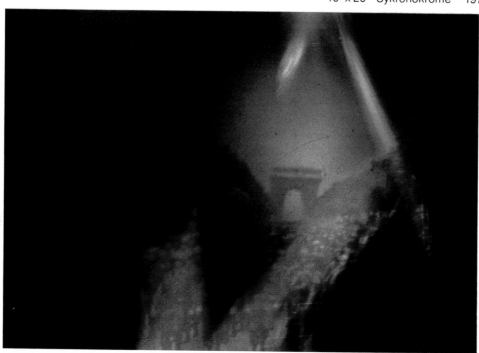

"V.E. NIGHT! PARIS" 16" x 16" Sykronokrome © 1978 $100.

impressario for other talents, a
critic and cultural advisor. Her
work here is also "moods" of live
and inert forms. "Sykronokromes"
©1977 is the name given to new
compositions of related events.

Of her work, the critics state:
"... she expresses the conscience
authority of the motif, and the
intimate echo that the eye of the
photographer gives mysteriously to
the work of the lens." Robert
Vrinat, Paris-1976
"... of Paris stormy vision,
'crepusculaire' under heavy clouds
and sky which she expresses in a
very pictural spirit." Denis Roger,
Carrefour, Paris-1976
"... Ligoa Duncan presents a
statue of LaFayette seen from afar,
a masterpiece of surrealism!"
Henri Heraut, L'Amateur d'Art-1976

"TV STAR CAROL BURNETT"
24" x 30" Oil on Canvas NFS

GALLERY:
   The Den of Color, Chicago, Illinois

EXHIBITIONS:
   Old Town Outdoor Art Fair, Chicago, Ill.
   Leon's Supper Club, Holiday Florida
   Palm Beach Hotel, Palm Beach, Florida
   Showboat Lounge, Three Lakes, Wisconsin
   Galerie d'Art, Paris, France

ASTOUNDING the art world at 16, Mr. Ebbert's portraiture and black and white illustrations have been widely acclaimed in Chicago, Florida, Wisconsin and Washington, D.C.

Born in poverty and self-taught, his famous images of Presidents Franklin D. Roosevelt and John F. Kennedy, as well as "Miss America 1973," appeared in previous editions of ARTISTS/USA and enjoy historical recognition and exposure in national shrines. The midwesterner's portrait of President Carter brought an encouraging acknowledgment from the White House. His biography appears in the 1978-79 editions of *Who's Who in the Midwest* and *Who's Who in American Art.*

The talented Chicagoan has spent years capturing on canvas the total personalities of VIP's in government, show biz and the professions.

EBBERT, GEORGE C.
616 N. Rush St.
Chicago, Illinois 60611

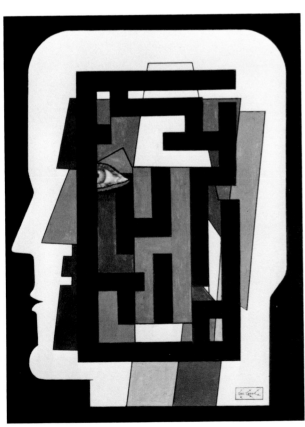

"ECCENTRIC SCHIZO" (A Jekyll/Hyde personality)
10½" x 13½" Acrylic/Watercolor on Poster Board POR

"THE DEVIL'S TRIANGLE" Legendary force of evil
in Barbados 8½" x 11" Crayon Pencil $85.; prints $3.

"CARL" 14" x 18" Oil
Collection of Mr. & Mrs. Carl L. Tagge

ELIASON, BIRDELL
12 North Owen Street
Mount Prospect, Illinois 60056

GALLERY:
Carriage Trade Interiors
276 Long Grove Road
Long Grove, Illinois 60047

EXHIBITIONS:
Art Institute of Chicago
McCormick Place, Chicago
Gold Coast, Invitational
Randhurst, Invitational
Civic Center, Chicago
Mid-Continental Plaza, Chicago
Lurtheran Gen. Hospital, Park Ridge
Northwest Dental Assn.
American Cancer Society
and many other regional shows

AWARDS:
Portland, Oregon, Grand Prize
State of Oregon, 2nd Place
Natl. PTA, Best of Show, Chicago
N.W. District, Gold Medal
Bicentennial Award, Garage Door
Scenes of Mt. Prospect, 17 awards
and numerous other awards

COLLECTIONS:
Mt. Prospect Historical Society,
    Mural-Mt. Prospect Indian history
Portraits of many prominent persons
    throughout the U.S.
Represented in public and private
    collections throughout the U.S.,
    Europe, S. Africa, Morocco & Mexico

"FALL IN NEW SALEM" 16" x 20" Oil POR

"JAMES JOYCE"
32" x 36"
Oil $1,500.

EGAN, JACQUES L.
809 N. Broad St.
Adrian, Michigan 49221

EXHIBITIONS:
Toledo Museum Annuals,
Ohio, 6 years
Oeste Gallery, N.Y.C.,
one-artist show
Fla. Southern College
New Directions, N.Y.C.
and others

AWARDS:
Fla. Southern College,
Blue Ribbon Award
Toledo Museum, Purchase Aw.

COLLECTIONS:
Toledo Museum Collection-
Numerous private colls.
throughout the U.S.

"THE MADHATTER" 7" x 18"
Rapidiograph Pen POR

FELTON, LORI K.
1401 Allston
Houston, Texas 77008

GALLERY:
Patricia Covo
4817 Montose
Houston, Texas 77006

EXHIBITIONS:
Chattanooga Exbt, Tn.
Two-Headed Wooden Nickel
Exbt, Houston, Texas
and numerous 1-artist
shows throughout Colo.

AWARDS:
Outstanding Exhibitor,
Houston, Texas
Pratt Inst., Brooklyn,
Advancement Award
and others

COLLECTIONS:
Texas Eastern Corp.
Educational Testing
Center, N.J.
and many private
throughout the U.S.

"ROAD TO JENNY LAKE" 30" x 40" Oil on Canvas $3,500.

FAY, KEITH L.
Box 1116
Jackson Hole, Wyoming 83001

BORN:
Scottsbluff, Nebraska; 1920

EXHIBITIONS:
3 one-artist shows in Southern
Calif. sponsored by Crocker
Banks
Jackson Lake Lodge, Grand Teton
National Park, 1-artist show

AWARDS:
Featured in Christian Science
Monitor

COLLECTIONS:
Private collections worldwide
including:
Robert Goulet
Roger Mudd
Mr. & Mrs. William Semones
Mr. & Mrs. Clark Williams
Dr. & Mrs. Meade Davis, III
Dow Chemical
Crocker Banks of Calif.
Borden Co.
Norris Industries
Wright Package, Inc.
Leanin Tree Publishing Co.

FERRIE, THOMAS J.
93 Pineland Avenue
Worcester, Mass.

GALLERY:
Treasures, Inc.
Art Center
Worcester, Mass.

EXHIBITIONS:
Many portraits in
private collections

Born in Worcester, Mass., Thomas J. Ferrie studied art at the Art Institute of Boston and also in Worcester. He has exhibited throughout New England and New York, displaying oil and pastel portraits and drawing portraits in charcoal and pastel at the shows. At his Worcester studio, Mr. Ferrie does oil portraits from commissions. He is also retained to paint all present and past presidents of a private organization in Shrewsbury, Mass. Spending between five and eleven hours on each oil painting, the artist works on toned linen canvas in two ½ hour sittings. He is a member of the International Society of Artists and a private art group in Boston.

"KIKI" 9" x 12" Charcoal on White Paper
Collection: Mr. & Mrs. Edward Hall

"SOLO" 8" x 10" Pastel on Black Paper NFS

FILIPPONE, BASIL
74 Christine Drive
E. Hanover, N.J. 07936

GALLERY:
The Artery
472 Bloomfield Ave.
Caldwell, N.J. 07006

EXHIBITIONS:
Univ. of Nebraska, Omaha
Joslyn Art Museum, Omaha

Richmond Prof. Inst., Va.
Virginia Beach, Va.
The Artery, 1-artist show
and many others

COLLECTIONS:
Many public & private

"HIDDEN DREAMS" 18" x 24" Pastels POR

"MORNING MIST" 18" x 24" Pastels POR

FINSON, HILDRED A.
304 S. Wilson
Jefferson, Iowa 50129

Hildred A. Finson is the author and illustrator of two published children's books.

EXHIBITIONS:
1-artist & group exhibits

"PSEUDO" 24" x 30" Oil on Canvas

FOLLETT, MARY V.
1440 Park Avenue
River Forest, Ill. 60305

GALLERY:
Paintin' Place
181 S. Oak Park Ave.
Oak Park, Ill. 60302

EXHIBITIONS:
Academy of Fine Arts,
Palette & Chisel
Municipal Art League
of Chicago

Oak Park Art League
and many others

AWARDS:
Union League of Chicago,
Civic & Arts Award
Many 1st & 2nd places
& honorable mentions

COLLECTIONS:
Collections throughout the
Midwest, California,
Florida & Europe

"DAWN ON THE GOLDEN GATE" 24" x 36" POR

FOOTE, J. LANELL
137 S. 2nd, East
Brigham City, Utah 84302

GALLERY:
Lanell's Studio
No. 8 West Forest
Brigham City, Utah 84302

EXHIBITIONS:
Utah State Fair, S.L.C.
Brigham City Peach Days
Z.C.M.I., Ogden, Utah

AWARDS:
Brigham City Peach Days,
First Place

COLLECTIONS:
Box Elcher School Dist.,
Brigham City, Utah
Many private collections

"MIRROR LAKE" $500.

FREDERIKSEN, ARNI
70 Willow St.
Brooklyn Hgts., N.Y. 11201

EXHIBITIONS:
One-artist shows:
Am. Scandinavian Fdn, NY
Royal Copenhagen
Porcelain, N.Y.
1st Fed. Loan Assoc., NY
Denver Art Museum

A.S.F., for H.M. Queen
Margrethe 2nd & H.R.H.
Prince Henrik of Denmark

COLLECTIONS:
J.C. Penney Art Coll.

COMMISSIONS:
Kennedy Center, Wash., DC
Helen Hayes Theater, N.Y.

"TWO KINGS" 64" x 59" Private collection

FRANKENTHALER, HELEN
173 E. 94th St.
New York, N.Y. 10028

BORN:
New York, N.Y., Dec. 12, 1928

EXHIBITIONS:
Whitney Museum of Am. Art, N.Y.
Los Angeles Museum of Art
Metropolitan Museum of Art, N.Y.
Museum of Fine Arts, Boston
Numerous one-artist shows

"MAUVE DISTRICT" 1966 Synthetic polymer paint on canvas 8'7" x 7'11"
Collection, The Museum of Modern Art, N.Y.
Mrs. Donald B. Straus Fund

FREEMAN, FRED L.
2949 Lilac Road
Beloit, Wisconsin 53511

GALLERY:
Burpee Gallery of Art
Rockford, Illinois 61103

"HARBOR SCENE I" 24" x 36" Oil $200.

GARDINER, PAULINE S.
P.O. Box 473
Seabrook, Texas 77586

GALLERIES:
Billingsley Gallery
1922 Strawberry
Pasadena, Texas 77502
Numerous others in Texas

BORN:
Salem, Oregon

EXHIBITIONS:
Watercolor Soc. of Houston
Gulf Coast Charity Arabian
Horse Shows

COLLECTIONS:
Private collections
worldwide, including:
Australia, New Zealand
England & N. Ireland

"THE 'MARY GALE' AT SEABROOK" Watercolor Limited
Edition-1000 $36.

GAZONAS, ALEXANDER G.
2 Commodore Road
Worcester, Mass. 01602

EXHIBITIONS:
Am. Watercolor Soc.
Annuals, 5 times
Mainstreams '73, Ohio
Academic Artists Assoc.,
Springfield, Ma., 4
Am. Artists In Paris Exbt.
1st Annual American Artist
Magazine Exbt., N.Y.

AWARDS:
Silver Medal of Honor,
Gloucester, Mass.

Robb Sagendorph Memorial
Award, Boston
Murial Ritchie Award,
Springfield, Ma.
American Artists Magazine
Competition, Finalist
Am. Watercolor Soc., N.Y.,
2 Travel Awards
Texas Fine Arts Assoc.
and many others

COLLECTIONS:
Corporate & private colls.

"MOTIF #2—ROCKPORT, MASS." 21" x 14" Watercolor

"THE SCULPTOR'S EXHIBITION #5"
8¼" x 7" Printing Ink on Paper POR

GENTILE, JOHN O.
114 Corbett Road
Stoughton, Mass. 02072

GALLERY:
Loft Gallery, 69 Harvey St.
Cambridge, Mass. 02140

EXHIBITIONS:
Grand Prix Intl. D'Art
Contemporain, Monte Carlo
West Broadway Gallery,
Exchange Show, N.Y.
Italian Heritage Exbt.,
Boston City Hall

Old Hwy Galleria, Cape Cod
and many others

AWARDS:
Grand Prix Intl. D'Art
Contemporain, Monte
Carlo, UNESCO Prize-1976

COLLECTIONS:
Natl. Museum of Monaco,
Perm. Coll., Monte Carlo
Several private colls. in
the U.S. & Italy

GATES, SHARON LEE
7003 East Cheney Drive
Scottsdale, Arizona 85253
GALLERY:
Studio Ranch Gallery
7003 East Cheney Drive
Scottsdale, Arizona 85253
    Visitors Welcome

"SUNRISE MOUNTAIN WRANGLERS" 24" x 30" Oil P(

"HARD SCRABBLE TRAIL" 24" x 30" Oil POR

GATES, SHARON LEE

"SAN FRANCISCO PEAKS" 16" x 20" Pastel POR

"CHIEF SHAKTA BEARSTEP" 30" x 40" Pastel POR

ADAM AND EVE 7¾" x 4" x 3½" Bronze*

CONTEMPLATION Boy, Girl or pair 7" x 4¾" x 2½" each Bronze*

GELLER, BUNNY
13 Oakdale Drive
Westbury, N.Y. 11590

GALLERIES:
Lynn Kottler Galleries
 3 E. 65th St.
 New York, N.Y. 10021
Intl. Treasury of Fine Art
 100 Fairchild Ave.
 Plainview, N.Y. 11803
Hollywood Art Museum
 2015 Hollywood Blvd.
 Hollywood, Florida 33020
Deligny Art Galleries
 709 E. Las Olas Blvd.
 Ft. Lauderdale, Fla. 33301

MOTHERHOOD (Front View) 5¾" x 3½" x 2¾" Bronze*

MOTHERHOOD (Back View)*

GRANDPA'S GIRL 18½″ x 16½″ x 8¾″ Bronze*

OUR GRANDMA 9″ x 5¼″ x 4½″ Bronze*

GELLER, BUNNY

GRANDMOTHER AND CHILDREN
15″ x 9″ x 7½″ Bronze*

SHOFAR 16¾″ x 13½″ x 18″ Bronze*

MERMAID (WATERFALL-FOUNTAIN) 15½" x 12" x 10½" Bronze*

DISCUS THROWER 18" x 5" x 13½" Bronze*

GELLER, BUNNY

SWEETHEARTS 5¾" x 6½" x 3¼" Bronze*

THE ETERNAL FEMALE 14½" x 11½" x 5" Bronze*

GELLER, BUNNY

FREE SPIRIT 22″ x 12″ x 20″ Bronze*

SPIRIT OF RUFFIAN 10¾″ x 15″ x 4½″ Bronze*

TÉTE-A-TÉTE 11½″ x 5″ x 8″ *

RUBY 12″ x 8″ x 10″ Bronze*

"THE SCARECROW" 1976 18" x 24" Oil on Canvas POR

"THE WINTER" 1977 18" x 24" Oil on Canvas POR

"SUNRISE" 1976 12" x 16" Oil on Canvas POR

"RELIFE" 1976 28" x 36" Oil on Canvas POR

GHAMDI, MOHAMMED S.
284 12th Avenue, #1
San Francisco, California 94118

BORN:
Al-Madina, Saudi Arabia,
Aug. 22, 1950

"LIFE OF THE FIELDS" 1977 24" x 32" Oil on Canvas POR

GHAMDI, MOHAMMED S.

"SELF-PORTRAIT" 1977 48" x 36" Oil on Canvas POR

"SKULL ON THE GRASS" 1977 12" x 16" Oil on Canvas POR

"MY FATHER'S DEATH" 1977
24" x 36" Oil on Canvas POR

GERARD, BARBARA

1623 Third Avenue
New York, N.Y. 10028

Studio:
598 Three Mile Harbour Rd.
Easthampton, L.I., N.Y.

GALLERY:
Viridian Gallery
24 W. 57th, N.Y.C. 10019

EXHIBITIONS:
One-artist shows:
Viridian Gallery, N.Y.
Henry Hicks Gall., N.Y.

N.E. Univ., Boston, Mass.
Womanart Gallery, N.Y.
Union Carbide, N.Y.
Lincoln Center, N.Y.
Union of Maine Artists, Me.
and others

COLLECTIONS:
BBDO Advertising Corp, NY
Museum Contemp. Crafts, NY
American Airlines Corp.
Many other public & private

"SUR LA PLAGE" 30" x 40" Acrylic & Sand POR

"YOUNG BEAUTY" 18" x 24" Pastel POR

GIFFUNI, FLORA B.

180-16 Dalny Road
Jamaica, N.Y. 11432

GALLERIES:
Reyn, 680 Madison Ave.
New York, N.Y. 10021
Petrenko Gallery
1045 Madison Ave.
New York, N.Y. 10021

EXHIBITIONS:
Am. Artists Prof. League
C.L. Wolfe Art Club
Natl. Arts Club-Salmagundi

AWARDS:
Grand Central Gal., AAPL
Natl '78, 1st Prize
Pastel Soc. of America
and others

GOMER, GARY

Park Towne Place North
Philadelphia, Pa. 19130

EXHIBITIONS:
Seagull Gallery,
Ship Bottom, N.J.
Port O'Call,
Ship Bottom, N.J.

Photograph 7½" x 9½" POR

GONZALEZ, RICHARD DANIEL ("RICARDO")

967 D. St.
Hayward, California 94541

EXHIBITIONS:
Numerous group & one-artist shows
in Spain, France, Argentina,
Brazil, Mexico & the U.S.

AWARDS:
Top awards in intl., natl.,
& regl. art competitions

COLLECTIONS:
Hayward City Hall, Calif.
Centennial Hall, Hayward, Ca.
Hayward Historical Museum, Ca.
The Daily Review, Hayward, Ca.
Murals in collections of:
San Leandro Cmmnty. Center, Ca.
Alameda County Fair
Project Eden, Hayward, Ca.
YWCA, Hayward, Ca.
Service Opportunity for Seniors,
Inc., Hayward, Ca.
Family Tutorial Program, Hayward
Mexicali-Rose Restaurant,
Oakland, Ca.
Mexicali-Rose #2, Alameda, Ca.
Maria Elena's Restaurant,
Concord, Ca.
Valley Matador Bar,
Castro Valley, Ca.
Numerous paintings in restaurants
& bars throughout Calif. and
many portraits & paintings in
private collections in Spain,
France, Argentina, Brazil,
Mexico & the U.S.

"THE EVILS OF THE ABUSE OF DRUGS" 6' x 10' Acrylic

GRAZIANO, MERCOLINO FLORENCE

1413 Highland Avenue
Plainfield, N.J. 07060

GALLERIES:
O'Toole & Sloan Galleries, N.Y.
Venice
Pebble Beach Gallery, Calif.
G & G Gallery, Plainfield, N.J.
Corral Gallery, Flemington, N.J.
Chase Gallery, N.Y.C.

EXHIBITIONS:
One-artist shows:
Wash. Co. Museum of Fine Arts, Md.
Sheldon Swope Art Gallery, Ind.
The Chase Gallery, N.Y.C.
Pebble Beach Gallery, Calif.
State University of N.Y.
The Press Box Gallery, N.Y.
Allied Artists
American Watercolor Society
Salon Des Beaux Arts, Paris
Festival des St. Germain, Des Pres
Biennial Print Show, Albany, N.Y.
National Arts Club Print Show, N.Y.
National Arts Club
Watercolor & Oil Shows, N.Y.
Jersey City Museum, N.J.
Salmagundi Club, N.Y.

AWARDS:
St. Germain des Pres, Brussels,
Gold Medal, 1973
Pen & Brush Club, N.Y.C.
1974 Oil & 1975 Graphics
AAPL, Bergen County Museum, N.J.,
1st in Oils

Westfield Art Association, N.J.,
2nd in Pastels
Wash., D.C. Hilton Art Show,
1st in Oils, 1st in Sculpture
Convention Hall Art Exbt.,
Las Vegas, 1st in Oils
Pen & Brush Club, N.Y., Oil Show 1976,
Award for Oil
Circolo Dell'Arte, Italy, 1st in Oils

COLLECTIONS:
Wash. Co. Museum of Fine Arts

Sheldon Swope Museum of Art, Ind.
University of Maine
Rutgers University, N.J.
N.Y. City College
Eisenhower College, N.Y.
Columbus College, Ohio
Beaver College, Pa.
Borden & Co., Columbus, Ohio
State University, Alfred, N.Y.
Purdue Univ., W. Lafayette, Ind.
Many private collections worldwide

"THE MONOPOLY GAME" 40" x 52" Oil

"SCOUT 1872" 21¼" high Bronze
1 through 15 numbered limited edition
Low numbers 1 thru 5—Piece $1,850.
Numbers 6 thru 15—Piece $1,350.

"APACHE" 13¾" high
Clay original NFS
Bronze, Numbered limited edition, 1 thru 25
Low numbers 1 thru 7—Piece $3,250.
Numbers 8 thru 25—Piece $2,750.

"RIDING A CIRCLE" 17" high x 22½" long
Clay original NFS
Bronze—Piece $2,300.

GREEN, VINCE

31961 Trevor Avenue
Hayward, California 94544

Sculpture, painting and drawing instructor, Vince Green,
through a consuming interest in our early American
Western culture, vividly brings alive in his art the
aura of that exciting period.

From a keen eye for detail, his works carry the distinc-
tion of authenticity so desired by students of our past
historic West. Commissions are accepted.

Bronzes on walnut base, brass inscription plate.

GOSNEY, N. RUTH

271 S. 6th St.
Middleport, Ohio 45760

GALLERIES:
Riverby Gallery,
.Gallipolis, Ohio
Huntington Gallery, W. Va.
Columbus Art Gallery, Ohio

COLLECTIONS:
Numerous public & private
throughout 4 states

"GETTING TO KOWN YOU" 9" x 12"
Ink Drawing, Limited Prints - $40.

N. Ruth Gosney, a free lance
traveling artist, is a member of
the Cowboy Hall of Fame in
Oklahoma City. She studied under
Prof. Dwight Mutchler at Ohio
University in Athens, Ohio.
Limited prints of her works are
available at $40. each.

"THE ATTIC" 20" x 24" Oil, Limited Prints - $40.

"I REMEMBER WHEN" 9" x 12"
Ink Drawing, Limited Prints - $40.

"HUMPBACK BRIDGE — VINTON COUNTY"
20" x 24" Oil, Limited Prints - $40.

GREGORIO, FRANK
7547 W. Monroe St.
Niles, Illinois 60648

BORN:
Laurino, Italy;
Nov. 15, 1884

EXHIBITIONS:
Tampa Bay Art Center-1977
Hillsborough County Art Festival-1977
Hillsborough County Art Festival-1978

AWARDS:
Hillsborough County Art Festival,
Award of Merit-1978

The artist at work

"SCULPTURES"

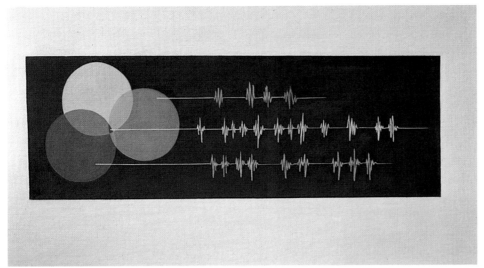

"IN THE BEGINNING WAS THE WORD" 1978 20" x 15" Oil©

GREGORIO, PETER A.
304 E. Davis Blvd
Tampa, Florida 33606

EXHIBITIONS:
  American Painters in Paris
  Rochester Festival of Religious
    Arts, N.Y.
  Beaux Art Guild, Tuskeege, Ala.
  Hillsborough County Art Festival
  Art Assoc. of Newport

AWARDS:
  Hillsborough County Art Festival,
    Award of Merit-1977

COLLECTIONS:
  Vatican Library, Rome

Peter A. Gregorio is a member of the
American Society of Artists, The
Graphic Society and the International
Society of Artists. He is listed in
Who's Who in the South and Southwest.

"YBOR CITY, TAMPA"
1978 20" x 30" Oil ©

"ERIK" 1978 18" x 24" Oil©

"CHRIST DISPUTING WITH THE DOCTORS"
1978 20" x 16" Oil©

GROTEY, GARY

‰ Artco, Incorporated
Rt. 2 - Box 109 Cuba Road
Long Grove, Illinois 60047

GALLERY:
    Merrill Chase Galleries
        Water Tower Pl., Chicago, Illinois

EXHIBITIONS:
    Pasadena Art Museum
    American Artists Convention, Houston
    Numerous one-artist & gallery shows

AWARDS:
    Pikes Peak Intl. Art Show, 1st Place Acrylics

COLLECTIONS:
    DePaul Univ. Art Museum, Chicago
    Mercantile National Bank, Chicago
    Over 200 private collections

Gary Grotey brings together layers of translucent transparencies and opaques to produce a three dimensional painting that refracts light in a manner that produces a wide range and intensity of color.

Grotey has combined a rare artistic sensitivity with an innate command of color and a marvelously live imagination. He uses pigments and resins (a plastic medium) to express himself in a unique way. His basic intentions are simple: Take a cold material and give it warmth, movement and a softness while achieving a balance of color intensities and tones unobtainable in any other media. Because of his concentrated efforts with this technique, Grotey has been able to transform raw materials into breathtaking works of abstract and realism in gloss resin, opening a new school within the realm of the art world.

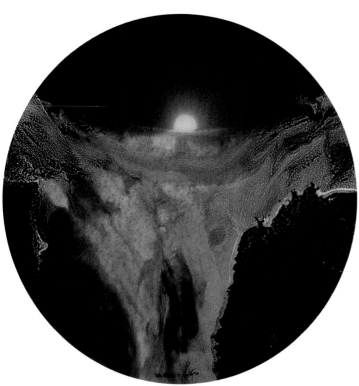

"MELTING REFLECTIONS" 3' Resin Painting POR

GUIDOTTI, JOHANNES S.

3600 Dawson
Warren, Michigan 48092

"SPRING ON THE RED PLANET"
16" x 22" Acrylic $150.

GUILLOUX, CHRISTINE

‰ Ligoa Duncan "Arts"
22 E. 72nd St.
New York, N.Y. 10021

EXHIBITIONS:
    Lousouve, Paris
    Salon des Surindependants
    Ligoa Duncan Gallery, N.Y.

Born in Paris in 1954, Christine Guilloux's studies were mainly directed towards art, creation and creativity. Specializing in pen and ink, she uses calligraphic techniques to express the deepness of emotion, sensation and feelings.

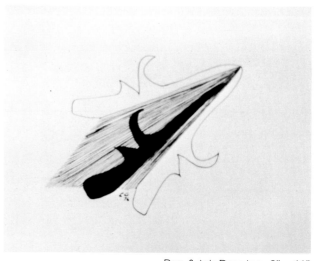

Pen & Ink Drawing 8" x 11"

GUNKEL, VIRGINIA P.

201 Freda Drive
Pacheco, California 94553

EXHIBITIONS:
  8 one-artist shows including:
    Lincoln University, Pa.
    Argent Gallery, N.Y.
    Barbizon Gallery, N.Y.
  Various juried shows including:
    Stedelijke Museum, Amsterdam
    Maison des Arts, Brussels
    Antwerp, Liege & Ostend
    Bern Art Museum, Switzerland
    American Gallery, Athens, Gr.
    L.M. Sweat Memorial Art Museum,
      Portland, Maine
    Norton Gallery, W. Palm Bch, Fla.
    Allied Artists of America,
      Natl Academy of Design, N.Y.
    Museum of Fine Arts, Boston

AWARDS:
  Painters & Sculptors Soc. of N.J.,
    Patron's Prize
  Natl Assoc of Women Artists,
    Jane C. Stanley Prize
  Terry Natl Art Exbt, Miami, Fla.
  Hofstra Univ., Hempstead, N.Y.

COLLECTIONS:
  N.Y. University Collection of
    Contemporary American Art
  Represented in private collections
    in U.S., Canada, Switzerland
    and Sweden

A member of the Society of Western Artists, Virginia Gunkel has been favorably reviewed twice in La Revue Moderne, Paris, France. She is listed in *Who's Who in American Women, Who's Who in American Art* and *Who's Who in America.*

"WIN, PLACE, SHOW" 11" x 15" Watercolor POR

HAFFORD, JEANNETTE C.

658 Columbia Ave.
Palmerton, Pa. 18071

GALLERY:
  Flemington Gallery
    of the Arts
  35 Mine St.
  Flemington, N.J. 08822

EXHIBITIONS:
  Lehigh Art Alliance,
    Allentown, Pa.

Les Beaux Art Gallery,
  Philadelphia, Pa.
Cedar Crest College,
  Allentown, 1-artist show
Baum Art School, Allentown
  and many other regl. shows

AWARDS:
  Baum School of Art, 3rd
    place, honorable ment.
  Country Show, 1st place

"WINTER WONDERLAND" 20" x 24" Oil POR

HAMANN, CAROL

GALLERY:
  Atlantic Gallery
  81 Atlantic Ave.
  Brooklyn, N.Y. 11201

EXHIBITIONS:
  Atlantic Gallery, 1-artist
  Salena Gall, LIU, 1-artist
  Cleveland Museum
  Brooklyn Museum

Wadsworth Atheneum,
  Hartford Art Museum
Womanart Gallery
Ct. Watercolor Society
Artists Equity Gallery
and many others

AWARDS:
  Womanart Gallery, Best of
    1977, First Prize
  Cleveland Museum, Purchase
    and others

"FLYING (BROOKLYN) BRIDGE"
14" x 16" Acrylic POR

HAMBLET, MARGARET WOOLDRIDGE

514 Lore Avenue
Wilmington, Delaware 19809

EXHIBITIONS:
San Francisco Art Assoc.
Western & Southeastern
Arts Assocs.
Pa. Academy of Fine Arts
Wilmington Soc. Fine Arts

COLLECTIONS:
Academic & private colls.

Margaret Wooldridge Hamblet received a BS in art from George Peabody College and a MA in art from the University of California. Her work has been published in *La Revue Moderne* in Paris. She is the illustrator of *Cindy-Puss,* a children's book.

"FAMILY PICNIC" 20" x 26" Oil NFS

HAVRILLA, JOHN R.

88 E. Maple St.
Tresckow, Pa. 18254

BORN:
Hazleton, Pa.; Oct. 10, 1956

COLLECTIONS:
Represented in numerous private collections throughout Pa., N.C. and Ill.

"WINTER'S TWILIGHT" 16" x 20" Acrylic POR

HARRIS, MURIEL B.

301 Plainfield Road
Edison, N.J. 00817

GALLERY:
Swain's Gallery
300 E. Front St.
Plainfield, N.J.

EXHIBITIONS:
One-artist shows:
Upper Gallery, Old Bridge, N.J.
Woodbridge Public Library, N.J.
Swain's Gallery, Plainfield
Edison Valley Playhouse, N.J.

Fanwood Memorial Library, N.J.
United Natl Bank, Plainfield
and others
Loeb Student Center, N.Y. Univ.
Hunterdon Art Center, Clinton
Somerset Art Assoc., N.J.
Many other natl & regl shows

AWARDS:
Bocour Award
Plainfield Natl Bank Award
Fairleigh Dickinson University,
Spectrum '76

"FORCE VS. BEAUTY, CREATIVITY, ETC."
30" x 42" Acrylic $850.©

COLLECTIONS:
Private, corp. & public collections

"DUNES, S. UTAH" 48" x 24" Acrylic $850.©

Found Object Sculpture

HARRISON, PHILIP
2714 Penn Towers
Philadelphia, Pa. 19103

EXHIBITIONS:
Art Alliance, Phila.
Main Line Center of Arts,
Haverford, Pa.
Warwick Gallery, Phila.

COLLECTIONS:
Many private collections in
N.Y.C., Phila., Palm Beach,
Chicago, Los Angeles &
throughout Europe

Philip Harrison, a found object
sculptor, works with wood,
electronic and automobile parts,
plastic, burlap and rope to
create sculpture and wall
constructions. His "sculpture to
wear" jewelry, combining natural
stones with electronic parts, is
available at the Mouche Boutique,
New York City and Palm Beach.

Wood Construction

HARTAL, PAUL
P.O. Box 1012
St. Laurent, Montreal
Quebec, H4L 4W3 Canada

GALLERY:
Ligoa Duncan Gallery
22 E. 72nd St. at Madison
New York, N.Y. 10021

A member of the Surindependants,
Musee du Luxembourg, Paris, Paul
Hartal is the inventor of a new
idea of art: LYRICAL CONCEPTUAL-
ISM, a poetic, intuitive and
interdisciplinary system. Its

creative process, projects and
iconography are based on the
dialectical integration of the
rational with the irrational.
Since Man is a symbol-making
being, Lyrical Conceptualism
advocates both abstraction and
figuration. Documentation in
books and periodicals functions
not merely as extension and
acceleration of communication,
but also as an additional form
of expression by means of
post-Guttenbergian media.

"STILL LIFE" 1977 18" x 24" Acrylic

"RISING BERGSONIAN CLOCK WITH MIGRATORY
GOLD FISH" 1977 18" x 24" Acrylic

HATFIELD, DAVID
240 West 38th Street
New York, N.Y. 10018

"BLUE HILL GROCERY" 24" x 20" Oil $1,500.

GALLERIES:
Grand Central Art Galleries
Biltmore Hotel
New York, N.Y. 10017
David Hatfield Gallery
11 Mt. Pleasant St.
Rockport, Mass. 01966
Christopher Gallery
766 Madison Ave., N.Y.C.

COLLECTIONS:
Many private collections

EXHIBITIONS:
National Academy of Design
Allied Artists of America
National Arts Club, 1-artist

AWARDS:
National Academy of Design,
Hallgarten Prize
Knickerbocker Artists, 1st Prize
Salmagundi Club, Peterson Prize
and many other top awards

"THE FRANKELS" 48" x 60" Oil NFS

HAYNES, KATHERINE H.
Star Rt. 3, Box 154
Bonners Ferry, Idaho 83805

GALLERIES:
The Art Studio
P.O. Box 1123
Lethbridge, Alberta T1J 4A4
Canada

Mushroom Gallery
W. 714 Sprague
Spokane, Washington 99201

Pine Log Studio
Star Rt. 3, Box 154
Bonners Ferry, Idaho 83805

"SUSANS" 16" x 20" Oil POR

"BERT'S PLACE" 15" x 22" Watercolor NFS

Born in Canada, Katherine Haynes
studied art at the University of
Alberta and the Banff School of
Fine Arts. She works in watercolors,
oils and acrylics.

Interests of Austin Hay have led him on many paths. His father was a physician and surgeon; his mother studied with William Merritt Chase and became a classmate and friend of Robert Henri.

In a life filled with creative people and a diversity of events, adventure beckoned. Following university days, the young scholarship student and four fellow musicians 'played' their way to Europe in the ship's orchestra. The ocean voyage took them to lands of colorful folk, spectacular scenery and legendary cities.

Ever since, the artist has envisioned travel as a kind of catalyst; infinite inspiration for developing a range of subjects. "Mood is important," he observes, "beauty of brushwork, quality of light." Whether it is a thatched-roof hut in islands of the Pacific or a medieval castle in highlands of Scotland, he is able to perceive and delight in an opportunity to document changing influences of history. "It is rewarding to see values—discovering always another way of representing passing appearances in a multi-faceted world."

HAY, GEORGE AUSTIN
President Monroe House
2017 Eye St., N.W.
Washington, D.C. (Winter)

National Arts Club
15 Gramercy Park
New York, N.Y. (Summer)

Hay Avenue
Johnstown, Pa. (Studio)

GALLERY:
Gallery Madison/90
1248 Madison Ave.
New York, N.Y.

EXHIBITIONS:
Pittsburgh Playhouse
Rochester Memorial Art Gallery
Columbia University
Parrish Art Museum, Southampton
Am. Artists Professional League
Manufacturers Hanover Trust
Riverside Museum
Duncan Galleries
Philharmonic Hall,
   Lincoln Center
Carnegie Institute
Am. Artists in Paris Exbtn.

AWARDS:
Prizes in regional exhibitions

COLLECTIONS:
University of Pittsburgh
Heller Memorial Foundation
U.S. Dept. of Transportation
Department of the Army
CBS
New York Public Library
Library of Congress
Metropolitan Museum of Art
Numerous private collections

"HOUSE ON THE HILL" 12" x 16" Oil, Collection: Howard Roberts. Freshness of summer pervades the graceful nature of this statement. Sunlight strides along a sweep of foreground. The big red house itself seems to provide contrasting relationship with verdant surrounding landscape. Strong vertical columns suggest dignity as well as a flavor of nostalgia.

HODGES, S.
830 East 14th
Ada, Oklahoma 74820

EXHIBITIONS:
Many one-artist shows
Many exbts in national
& regional shows

AWARDS:
Several awards in natl.
& regl. shows

COLLECTIONS:
Public & private colls.
in 38 states

S. Hodges' special interests
are (1) Rocky Mountain scenes
done with painting knives and
thick oil paint, and (2)
abandoned buildings and homes
and ghost towns, usually done
in watercolor.

"ABANDONED" 14" x 19" Watercolor POR

HOFFMAN, HARRY Z.
3910 Clark's Lane
Baltimore, Maryland 21215

BORN:
Baltimore, Dec. 5, 1908

EXHIBITIONS:
Albany Inst of Hist & Art
Pa. Academy of Fine Arts
Baltimore Museum of Art
Laguna Beach, Calif.
Galerie Internationale,
14 intl shows &
1-artist show, N.Y.
Many others

AWARDS:
Baltimore Natl Watercolor
Wash. Cnty Museum, 1st prize
Evening Sun Sketch Contest,
4 1st prizes
WCBM Award

COLLECTIONS:
Commun. College of Baltimore
Baltimore Museum of Art
Enoch Pratt Library
80 private collections

"RAWSON SQUARE-NASSAU"
36" x 48" Oil & Acrylics $2,500.

"APOCALYPSE"
30" x 40"
Acrylic on Canvas

HOUCK, PEGI
4th Avenue
Hastings, Pennsylvania 16646

COLLECTIONS:
Private throughout the U.S. & Europe

Pegi Houck received a BFA from Beaver College and an MA
from California State University, Los Angeles. She also
studied with Jossey Bilan and at Tyler School of Fine
Arts, Scripps in Claremont, California, Otis Art Institute
in Los Angeles, Naropa Institute in Boulder and in Europe.

HUDSON, JULIE H.
4224 Beverly Drive
Dallas, Texas 75205

GALLERIES:
Roughton Gallery, Dallas
Baker, Knapp & Tubbs, Dallas

AWARDS:
Many 1st awards in
juried shows

COLLECTIONS:
Private collections
in many states

"MERRY CHRISTMAS" 16" x 20" Acrylic NFS

"ROSA"
36" x 24"
Acrylic on Canvas
POR

IMANA, JORGE G.
2168 Chatsworth Blvd.
San Diego, Calif. 92107

GALLERY:
The Artists Showroom
2168 Chatsworth Blvd.
San Diego, Calif. 92107

EXHIBITIONS:
68 one-artist shows
Museum of Mod. Art, Paris

Madrid & Barcelona-1974
Poland, Rumania & USSR-1974

AWARDS:
San Diego Art Institute,
Purchase Awards
and several others in U.S.,
Bolivia & Peru

COLLECTIONS:
Public & private worldwide

"LIBERTY '76" From "KENT BICENTENNIAL
PORTFOLIO: SPIRIT OF INDEPENDENCE" 1975
38" x 34⅛" Serigraph, Collection: The Museum of
Modern Art, New York.
Gift of Lorillard, a division of Loews Theatres, Inc.

INDIANA, ROBERT
2 Spring Street
New York, N.Y. 10012

BORN:
New Castle, Indiana,
Sept. 13, 1928

GALLERY:
Galerie Denise Rene
6 W. 57th St.
New York, N.Y. 10019

"WINTER 1978" 24" x 48" Acrylic on Masonite NFS

EXHIBITIONS:
Univ. of Arkansas, Fayetteville
First National Bank of Eastern Ark.
Southland Mall, Memphis, Tenn.

COLLECTIONS:
Many private collections
throughout the U.S.
Many commissions

ISOM, JOHN E.
124 West Scott Avenue
Forrest City, Arkansas 72335

"LAKE WEDDINGTON" 10" x 14" Acrylic on Canvas Board $100.

JACKSON, HERBERT DAN

London Lane, Rt. 3
Ringgold, Georgia 30736

GALLERIES:
In-Town Gallery
Choo Choo Read House
Chattanooga, Tn 37402
Lighthouse Gallery
Gallery Square
Tequesta, Fla 33458

EXHIBITIONS:
Hunter Museum of Art, Tn.
High Museum, Atlanta
Many 1-artist & group shows

AWARDS:
Many awards in SE states

COLLECTIONS:
Burt Reynolds
Many public & private

JANELLE, RHEAUME

R.R. #2, Box 158
Danville, PQ, Canada JOA 1A0

GALLERY:
L'Estrie Gallery
Porland Blvd.
Sherbrooke, Canada

EXHIBITIONS:
Asbestos Art Center

Civic Arena, Richmond
Le Marquis, Richmond
and many others

AWARDS:
Best of Show & many othe

COLLECTIONS:
Many public & private in
Canada, U.S. & France

"BALLERINA II" Life Size Corten Steel POR

"THE SKATERS" 22" x 30" Oil POR

JARDINE, ELLEN A.

15 Hamilton Drive
Madison, Conn. 06443

Star Route
Marshfield, Vermont 05658

GALLERIES:
Pinch Penny Gallery
Essex, Conn. 06426
Schofield & Vose Gallery
Main St.
Branford, Conn. 06405

EXHIBITIONS:
Madison Medical Center
Madison, Ct., Continuous Show
Madison Art Society
Clinton Art Society
Lyme Art Society
Brush & Palette Club,
New Haven, Conn.
and many other regl. shows

COLLECTIONS:
Private collections
throughout the U.S.

Ellen Jardine is listed in the
International Directory of Arts-1978.

JENKINS, PAUL
31 E. 72nd St.
New York, N.Y. 10021

BORN:
Kansas City, Mo., July 12, 1923

EXHIBITIONS:
Art Institute of Chicago

Carnegie Institute, Pittsburgh
Corcoran Gallery of Art, Wash., D.C.
and many other group & 1-artist shows

COLLECTIONS:
Museum of Modern Art, N.Y.
Whitney Museum of Am. Art, N.Y.
Tate Gallery, London
Stedelyk Museum, Amsterdam

Museum of Western Art, Tokyo
and many others

Paul Jenkins studied at the Kansas City
Art Institute and School of Design and at
the Art Students League. His artwork was
featured in Twentieth Century Fox's motion
picture *An Unmarried Woman*.

"PHENOMENA: YELLOW STRIKE" 1963-64 60⅛" x 39⅞"
Synthetic polymer paint on canvas
Collection, The Museum of Modern Art, New York.
Gift of Mr. & Mrs. David Kluger.

JERMYN, ROBERT J.
3586 Powder Mill Rd.
Beltsville, Maryland 20705

EXHIBITIONS:
Washington, D.C. area
Military hospitals
VA hospital wards

AWARDS:
Honorary awards given
by military

COLLECTIONS:
Numerous public & private in
Wash., D.C., Md. & Va.

Robert Jermyn, a retired
Army master sergeant, studied
art for ten years while on
active duty. He belongs to
various art societies
throughout the country.

"THE EYE" 8" x 10" Oil, Pastels, Colors

"STORM AT SEA" 8" x 10"
Mixed Acrylic & Enamel

JOHNS, JASPER
225 E. Houston St.
New York, N.Y. 10002

BORN:
Augusta, Georgia, 1930

COLLECTIONS:
Tate Gallery, London
Museum of Modern Art, N.Y.
Whitney Museum of Am. Art, N.Y.
Albright-Knox Art Gallery
Wadsworth Atheneum, Ct.
Modern Museum, Stockholm

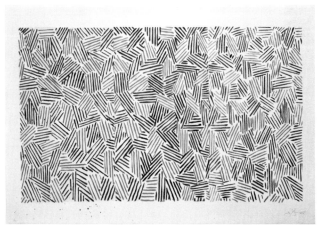

"SCENT" 1975-76 Lithograph, linoleum cut and woodcut,
printed in very red orange, deep green, medium violet,
yellow gray, embossed, comp (irreg.): 28½" x 44⅜"
Collection, The Museum of Modern Art, New York
Gift of Celeste Bartos

"THE ANDROGYNOUS
ANGEL"
14" x 16" Acrylic
$1,600.

JOHNSON, D. KENDRICK
P.O. Box 7162
Carmel, California 93921

EXHIBITIONS:
The Polygon, Cannery
Row, Calif.
Ann Arbor Assn., Mich.
and many others

AWARDS:
25 top awards

COLLECTIONS:
University of Kansas
San Bernardino Valley
College, Calif.
Naval Postgrad. School
Many private collections

JESSEN, SHIRLEY A.
90 Fifth Street
Garden City, N.Y. 11530

EXHIBITIONS:
One-Artist Shows:
N.Y. State Council on the Arts
Natl Bank of North America
Wantagh Library
S.E. Nassau Guidance Clinic
Security National Bank
Garden City Library
Cinema Theatre
7-12 Association
"Community Arts" Shows
Merrick Theatre
Reynolds Securities Inc.
Gallery
Nassau County Office of
Performing & Fine Arts
Juried Shows:
Salmagundi Art Club
"American Artist"
Locust Valley Juried Show
Banker's Trust Juried Show
Greenwich Savings Bank
YWCA Juried Show
Town Hall Juried Show, Hempstead

"WINKIN', BLINKIN' AND NOD" 24" x 36" Acrylic $200.

AWARDS:
"American Artist" First National
Arts Competition
N.Y. School of Applied Design
for Women Scholarship
Blue Ribbons

COLLECTIONS:
Private collections in
6 states

"APRÉS LA MER" 28" x 29" Oil $375.

"REFLECTION" 23" x 36" Oil $750.

JOHNSON, GWENAVERE A.
Tree Tops Studio
2054 Booksin Avenue
San Jose, Calif. 95125

GALLERIES:
San Jose Art Center
  482 S. Second St.
  San Jose, Calif. 95113
Los Gatos Art Gallery
  529 Santa Cruz Ave.
  Los Gatos, Calif. 95030

EXHIBITIONS:
One-artist shows:
  Los Gatos Art Gallery
  San Jose Art League
  Los Gatos Meadows Gallery
Los Gatos Art Gallery,
  1-family, 3-artist show
Soc. of Western Artists
Los Gatos Art Assn. Shows
San Jose Art League Shows
Livermore Festival of Arts
San Jose City Hall

"SERENGETI ZEBRAS" 24" x 36" Oil $220.

AWARDS:
Livermore Art Festival Awards
Annual Juried Valley Fair Artists Awards
Los Gatos Annual Juried Show Awards

COLLECTIONS:
Alexian Brothers Hospital
Many private collections

Gwenavere Johnson is a graduate of the Minneapolis School of Art and of the University of Minnesota, majoring in art. She has an M.A. degree in art education from San Jose State University and has taught in public and private secondary schools for thirty years.

"MANKIND" 24" x 36" Oil & Gold Leaf $220.

JOHNSON, JANICE E.
Route 1, Box 23
Erwin, North Carolina 28339

EXHIBITIONS:
Dunn Woman's Club Bicentennial
  Art Show, Dunn, N.C.
Spring Festival, Fayetteville, N.C.
Raleigh Woman's Club Art Show, N.C.

AWARDS:
1st place, Best in Show and others

"FALL IN THE VALLEY" 21" x 27" Acrylic POR

"THE TOREADOR"
8″ x 10″ Pen & Ink POR

Myrna Johnson has been quite active in various types of art projects since her grade school days. She has studied fashion illustration, watercolor, charcoal, pastels and pen and ink. Her favorite mediums are pen and ink and colored markers. While serving in the U.S. Navy, Miss Johnson had opportunities to work on charts, graphs, maps, blueprints, posters, a slide presentation for the U.S. Naval Air Reserve Program and many other art projects. Her work is represented in several private collections.

"BOY AND GIRL" 8″ x 10″ Pen & Ink POR

JOHNSON, MYRNA J.
1201 South Court House Road, Apt. 610
Arlington, Virginia 22204

"ENGLISH COUNTRYSIDE" 8″ x 10″ Pen & Ink POR

"ISLAND PARADISE" 8″ x 10″ Pen & Ink POR

"INDIAN" $200.

JONES, ERNEST LEE
1015 Elkin St.
Norfolk, Virginia 23523

BORN:
Virginia, Oct. 5, 1931

"PRAY MAN" $900.

"MEDITATION" 18″ high Teak

KAROL, REUBEN H.
261 S. Adelaide Ave.
Highland Park, N.J. 08904

GALLERIES:
Jeri Galleries
93 School Rd., West
Marlboro, N.J. 07746

Karl Mann Tunnel Gallery
232 E. 59th St.
New York, N.Y. 10022

EXHIBITIONS:
Rhoda Sande Gallery, N.Y.C.
Jeri Galleries, N.J.
Sol Del Rio, San Antonio

KARR, CHARLEE MARIE
4901 Garfield
Groves, Texas 77619

GALLERY:
Gallerie 546
1926 9th Ave.
Port Arthur, Texas 77640

EXHIBITIONS:
Beaumont Art Museum,
Texas, 1-artist show
Brown Scurlock Gallery,
1-artist show

Robert Brackman Students
Group Show, N.Y.

COLLECTIONS:
Represented in private
collections in N.Y.,
N.J., Colo., N.M., Tex.,
Minn., Wash.

Ms. Karr holds a B.A. in art
and is a life member of the
Art Students League of N.Y.
where she studied from
1945-1949.

"REFLECTIONS" 20″ x 30″ 1977 Acrylic
From Collection of Daud Harmon, Winnie, Texas

"BUDDAH" POR

KAMADA, ITOHEI
℅ Ligoa Duncan "Arts"
22 E. 72nd St. at Madison
New York, N.Y. 10021

Itohei Kamada has been very active these last few years, like a pilgrim, painting the sights in France that the French Impressionists painted before him. "Montagne Sainte Victoire" is an example of this East/West association of styles. He had several important exhibitions in Japan in 1977 and 1978 and is participating in one-artist shows of his recent paintings in Paris and New York. The artist has also become a member of the "Action Friends Committee" for the Centenary of Isadora Duncan/Raymond Duncan Exhibitions and is the organizer for the Japanese participation in 1979–80.

GALLERIES:
Raymond Duncan, Paris
Duncan-Echeverria Gallery,
Moorestown, N.J.

EXHIBITIONS:
Paris & N.Y. under the aegis of
Mumon Yamada Roshi
Salon des Artistes Francais
Grand Salon des Surindepen.
Acad. Intl. de Lutece, Paris

AWARDS:
Prix du Centenaire
Raymond Duncan, Paris
Belgo Hispanica Order of Merit,
Brussels
Grand Prix Humanitaire, Fr.

COLLECTIONS:
Musee des Beaux Arts de
Montbard, France

"BAMBOOS" POR

"MONTAGNE SAINTE VICTOIRE" POR

KAPRAL, PEGGY
Route 2, Box 370
Eatonville, Washington 98328

EXHIBITIONS:
Peoples Mortgage Co.
Puget Sound National Bank of Washington
and many other local & regional shows

COLLECTIONS:
Represented in public & private
collections in 19 states

"THE SANFORD BINION HOUSE, MILLEDGEVILLE, GEORGIA-Circa 1825"

"CONCORD, NATCHEZ, MISSISSIPPI" $14.

Peggy Kapral enjoys painting local scenery, including old barns, landscapes and seascapes in watercolor. A particular interest is drawing antebellum (pre-Civil War) homes of the "Old South" in pen and ink and making them into prints. Mrs. Kapral attends pilgrimages every year honoring the white-pillared mansions and the way of life that went along with them.

The artist also does Oriental brush paintings on rice paper and silk and sells pen and ink prints of various Victorian mansions throughout the U.S. Brochures are available.

"CHRISTMAS SCENE" 28" x 21"

"PUMPKIN—VEGETABLES" 20" x 28"

Roy Keister

KEISTER, ROY
15800 Highland Drive
San Jose, Calif. 95127

BORN:
Germantown, Ohio; Jan. 2, 1886

GALLERIES:
Gallery Tivoli
239 State St.
Los Altos, Calif. 94022
Bob French, Collector
348 Saratoga Ave.
San Jose, Calif. 95129

AWARDS:
Palette & Chisel Academy, Chicago,
Best Portrait of the Year
Intl Madona Festival, L.A., 2 awards
Laguna Beach Art Assn, 5 awards
and many others

Born in 1886, Roy Keister still works a full day, teaching and creating paintings. The author of an illustrated instruction book on painting, this versatile artist paints landscapes, portraits and still lifes, mainly in oils. Mr. Keister has created genre subjects of all tribes of Indians ("Trading Post" is illustrated). He has also painted many Indian chiefs in full bonnet life size. Several thousand copies of "Chief Joseph," printed on fine quality paper in full color, are available from the artist.

The State of Texas boasts a 23' x 13' mural by the artist in the Fort Brown Memorial Center in Brownsville. He has also done a ceramic mural of the same size for the beautiful garden near the Mural Building and Auditorium, depicting vegetation, flowers and bushes.

"TRADING POST" 30" x 50"

"DESERT STORM" 22" x 28" Oil

KENT, LESTER GRANT

22315 Western Blvd.
Hayward, California 94541

EXHIBITIONS:
Alemeda County Fair
Oakland Art Gallery
San Jose State College
Columbia, Calif.
Crow Canyon Chateau
International Kitchen
Vallejo Art Show
Santa Cruz Art Assoc. Show

AWARDS:
Alemeda County Fair, awards
for several years
Calif. State Fair, Block
Print Award

COLLECTIONS:
3 paintings in Hayward
Historical Society
Permanent Exhibit

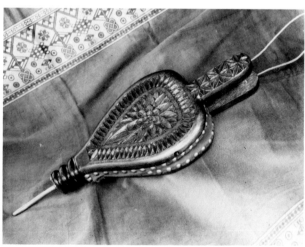

"CARVED FIREPLACE BELLOWS" 8" x 22"

"ST. JAMES CHURCH—SINORA, CALIF." Pen & Ink

"CARVED JEWEL CHEST" 8" x 12" x 7" High

"SEAGULL" 20" x 25"

KNIGHT, JAY
36 Hanrahan Avenue
Farmingville, L.I., N.Y. 11738

BORN:
Rockville Center, L.I., N.Y.;
May 28, 1950

GALLERY:
Fine Arts Academy
1600 Railroad Avenue
Holbrook, L.I., N.Y. 11742

EXHIBITIONS:
Fine Arts Academy, Holbrook,
L.I., N.Y.-June, 1978
Christophers Galleries, N.Y.
Smithtown Township Arts Council Show
St. Johns Hospital, Smithtown, N.Y.
Smithaven Mall, Lake Grove, N.Y.
Sunrise Mall, Massapequa, N.Y.
Winter Arts Festival 1978,
Bethpage State Park, L.I., N.Y.
Suburban Art League Membership Show,
Bethpage State Park, L.I., N.Y.
LIRRMTA Art Show, Madison Sq. Garden
and others in L.I. and N.Y.

AWARDS:
Winter Arts Festival, Honorable
Mention-1977–78
LIRR-MTA Art Show, 3rd Place-1978
Smithtown Artist of Month, Aug., 1973

COLLECTIONS:
St. Johns Hospital, Smithtown, N.Y.
Mr. & Mrs. James R. Knight
Mr. & Mrs. C.H. Boyle
Diane Holop
Karen (Lady Magnolia) Knight
Mr. & Mrs. Michael Knight

Jay Knight received his art training at
Lindenhurst High School, Sachem High
School and Suffolk Community College. He
has also taken advanced studies under
Gail Fitzer and Ken Burke. The artist is
a member of the Suburban Art League and
president of the Basement Art Group.

The artist is an emotionalist, working
in a realistic, surrealistic style in
sculpture and a real surrealistic,
pointalist style in painting.

"INSIGHT, INCITE" 21" x 12"

KEPP, CAROL S.

810 Ivanhoe Drive
Port St. Lucie, Fla. 33452

GALLERY:
River Gallery of Arts
19056 Detroit Road
Rocky River, Ohio 44116

EXHIBITIONS:
One-artist shows:
Elliott Museum of Stuart
Art Assocs. of Martin Co.

Group shows:
Lighthouse Gallery
Ft. Pierce Art Gallery

AWARDS:
D.A.R. Bicentennial Show,
Best of Show
Many other top awards

COLLECTIONS:
Numerous public & private
in U.S. & Canada

"EXXES FARM" 24" x 30" Oil $250.

KNAPP, VIRGINIA

Ring Neck Road
Drawer H
Remsenburg, N.Y. 11960

EXHIBITIONS:
E. Islip Publ. Library, N.Y.
Sayville Yacht Club, N.Y.
La Petite Gallery, N.Y.
One-artist shows:
Golden Bough Gallery, N.Y.
Castle Gallery, N.Y.
and others

COLLECTIONS:
Brookhaven Mem. Hosp., N.Y.
Golden Bough Gallery
Numerous private colls.

Virginia Knapp's work appeared
on the cover of *Artist's
Forum.* Numerous posters.

"MAN TRAVELING THROUGH INFINITY"
Private collection

KUNARD, ROBBIE C.

677 42nd Avenue
San Francisco, Calif. 94121

BORN:
San Francisco, Nov. 20, 1926

GALLERY:
Scott Gallery
107 Orinda Way
Orinda Village, Calif. 94563

EXHIBITIONS:
Frye Museum, The Society of
Western Artists
Exhibited regularly with The
Society of Western Artists
for 7 years

AWARDS:
U.S. Attorney's Office (SWA),
San Francisco, 2nd Award-
Watercolors-1978
Fresno Fashion Fair, 2nd Place-
Pastels-1978

Born in San Francisco, Robbie
Kunard's babysitter as a child was
a Siberian wolf. Always around
animals and loving to paint, she
started the idea of "pet portraits."
It was in Bangkok, Thailand where
Mrs. Kunard became interested in
painting exotic animals, her
favorite being the tiger. As a
member of the Society of Western
Artists, she gives demonstrations
in the public schools and is the
San Francisco representative for
the International Society of Artists.
The artist accepts commissions for
pet portraits from all over the
world.

"SAMOYED DOG" 16" x 20" Pastel $125.

"NO. 16" 18" x 24" Pastel NFS

KOLAWOLE, LAWRENCE COMPTON

357-B Scott Street
San Francisco, Calif. 94117

BORN:
Beaumont, Texas; Aug. 20, 1931

EXHIBITIONS:
S.F. Museum, Calif.
Muiska-Museum, Munchen,
   Permanent Kolawole Exbtn.
Galerie Schwetl, Furth
Brussels, 1-artist exbtn.
   on Art Actual
Galerie 55, Paris, 1-artist
Galerie Dimitrios, Amsterdam
Harbstsalon Hausder Kunst,
   Munich, Germany

Intl Art Market Paint Show,
   Dusseldorf, Germany
Several traveling shows, U.S.
   and many other one-artist &
   group shows throughout the
   U.S. & Europe

COLLECTIONS:
Leinbach Museum, Munich
Insel Film Gmb., Stadt
   Witten Museum, Munich
Nigerian Art Assoc, Lagos
Walter Baraiss, art expert
Th. Simon, brewery owner
Lenbach Gallery, Munich
City of Munich, Graphic Coll.

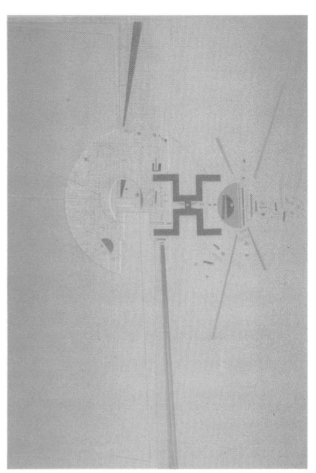

Untitled 23½" x 31½" Serigraph $300.

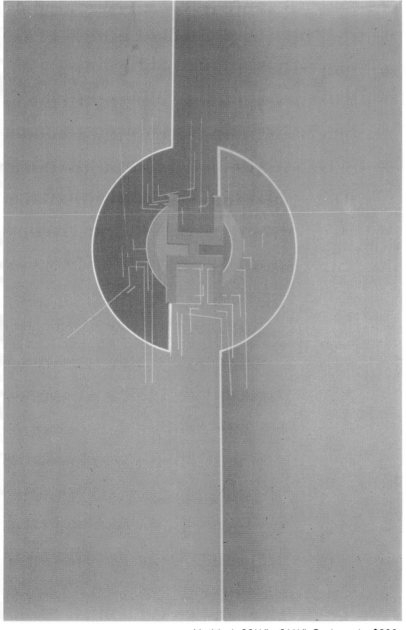

Untitled 23½" x 31½" Serigraph $300.

Lawrence Compton Kolawole is a painter, sculptor, and craftsman who has worked with oil pigments on canvas, stone, steel, magnasite, terracotta, wood, gold leaf, inks, silk screen printing and the materials of the etching process. Upon completion of his formal studies at the California School of Fine Arts, the artist began a series of travels which took him to New York, Munich, Nigeria and Paris. From boyhood, the artist was intensely curious about the history of people. In 1966, he found himself in Lagos, Nigeria, the area from which his people had come. Nigeria was in the chaos and terror of the Biafran war, but he remained, traveling throughout the country. There he observed and recorded in his mind the culture, the artifacts and symbols of his heritage. It was during this period of exploration and reflection that he was given his Nigerian surname, Kolawole.

The character of Kolawole's work is an amalgam of personal iconography, observed Nigerian imagery, and selected idiom from European art traditions. The artist draws upon a fund of mind-stored imagery from both his Western and African heritage, in an intuitive rather than calculated composition, to achieve what he names ''Motion Art.'' His intention is to capture the movement of the myriad forms that invest all life, rather than the compositional movement of Western tradition in the arts.

"J.C."
24" x 30"
Oil $950.

KNUTSON, DONALD L.
120 S. Martin
Visalia, California 93277

GALLERY:
American West
Carmel, California

EXHIBITIONS:
Ariz. State Univ., Tempe
Bartons Art Emporium,
Ariz., one-artist show
Ira Roberts Gallery,
Beverly Hills, Calif.

COLLECTIONS:
Gov. Dan Thorton, Colorado
Barry Goldwater, Jr., Ariz.
and others

LANGSTON, JUDY A.
1122 Kemman Avenue
La Grange Park, Illinois 60525

"UNTITLED" 5" x 7" Black & White Photograph POR

"THE GREEN WATER OF MONTEREY PENINSULA"
30" x 48" Oil POR

LAND, M. SCHWABEN
1375 Oak Avenue
Los Altos, California 94022

GALLERIES:
Brush & Palette
Los Altos, California 94022

Casa Dolores
Carmel-By-The-Sea, Calif.

AWARDS:
Society of Western Artists

M. Schwaben Land teaches at
International Art, Santa Clara,
California.

"THE PACIFIC BELOW SAN SIMEON" 30" x 48" Oil POR

"#1, SERIES 'M'" 1978

"#3, SERIES 'M'" 1978

LARSEN, BEN
832 Camino
Ranchitos,
Santa Fe,
New Mexico
87501

Paintings, wall
hangings and
serigraphs.

Illustrated, limi-
ted editions of 100
22" x 30"
Serigraphs on
Stonehenge
100% rag paper . . .
Prices on Request

"ELVIS" 18" High Wood Sculpture

"COMMODORE BATTON" 28" High Wood Sculpture

LaMONTAGNE, ARMAND

AGENT:
  Beverland Enterprises, Inc.
  P.O. Box 250, Dept. AR100
  Oldsmar, Florida 33557

GALLERY:
  Ace Powell Art Gallery
  Out Law Inn
  Kalispell, Montana 59901

COMMISSIONS:
  Ford Presidential Library,
    Commissioned to paint President Ford's
    portrait and sculpt the President's
    bust.
  Cowboy Hall of Fame, Commissioned to
    sculpt Walter Brennan.

A master woodsculptor and portrait artist, Armand LaMontagne was born in
the United States and studied sculpturing in Florence, Italy. His works
of art speak for themselves. Through the Paul King Foundry, LaMontagne
is creating some of the most valuable bronzes on the contemporary market.
His portraits in oils are magnificent. His sculptures in wood are the total
genius of the artist.

"LINCOLN" 28" High Wood Sculpture

"ELVIS" 18" High Bronze

LAUTTENBACH, CAROL
39 Ridgewood Road
Wallingford, Ct. 06492

AWARDS:
Salon of the 50 States,
  Prix de Paris Awards (2)
Mt. Carmel Art Assn., Best
  Ct. Landscape Prize
Drawing Anthology Intl.
  '74 Award, Long Island
Meriden Arts & Crafts Assn,
  1st Prize, Ct.

Guilford Art League, Ct.
Washington School of Art
  Intl Contest, N.Y.
Old Saybrook Summer Art
  Exbt, Ct.
Branford Art League, Ct.
Wallingford Art League,
  Ct., several awards
Autumn Outdoor Art Exbt.,
  Wallingford, Ct.
and others

"MY SHACK" 16½" x 23½" Oil POR

LEHRER, JACK C.
250 Park Ave., So.
New York, N.Y. 10003

EXHIBITIONS:
Allied Artists of America
Hudson Valley Art Assoc.
Salmagundi Club
National Arts Club
Kent Art Assoc., Ct.
Washington Art Assoc.
Am. Artists Prof. League
Elected artist member
  of above societies

AWARDS:
Numerous awards

COLLECTIONS:
Represented in public &
  private collections
  throughout the U.S.

"CONNECTICUT FARM" 20" x 24" Oil NFS

LEIPZIG, MEL
38 Abernethy Drive
Trenton, N.J. 08618

GALLERY:
Far Gallery
22 E. 80th St.
New York, N.Y. 10021

COLLECTIONS:
N.J. State Museum
Morris Museum
Cooper Hewitt Museum
A.T.&T.
and others

AWARDS:
N.J. Governor's
  Purchase Prize
Best in Show
Fulbright Grant
Louis Comfort Tiffany Award

74" x 44"
Acrylic
$6,000.

"FRANCESCA AT BREAKFAST"

"PASSAGE" 1960 9¼" x 6¼" x 5½"
Enamel on metal with marble base
Collection, The Museum of Modern Art, New York
Gift of Mr. & Mrs. Jan Mitchell

LIBERMAN, ALEXANDER
173 E. 70th St.
New York, N.Y. 10021

BORN:
Kiev, Russia, 1912

GALLERY:
Andre Emmerich Gallery
41 E. 57th St.
New York, N.Y. 10028

COLLECTIONS:
Museum of Modern Art, N.Y.
Whitney Museum of Am. Art, N.Y.
Tate Gallery, London
National Collection of Fine Arts,
  Washington, D.C.
and many others

LEIGHNINGER, PEGGY
1124 Midway Road
Northbrook, Illinois 60062

GALLERIES:
The Pat Whipple Gallery
2200 Waukegan Road
Glenview, Illinois 60025

The Brewery Works Fine Arts Salon
W 62, N 718 Riveredge Drive
Cedarburg, Wisconsin 53012

EXHIBITIONS:
Watercolor West, Riverside, Calif.
Miniature Painters, Sculptors &
Gravers Society, Wash., D.C.
Springville Museum of Art, Utah
Museum of the Great Plains,
Lawton, Oklahoma
Spar Natl Art Exbt, Shreveport, La.
Brownville Art League, Texas
Miniature Art Society of N.J.
Women in the Arts, West Bend, Wisc.
American Natl Miniature Show,
Laramie, Wyoming
Miniature Art Society of Florida

AWARDS:
3 National, 3rd prize-watercolor
15th Annual Barrington Art Fair
6th Annual Natl Art Show,
La Junta, Colorado
Rock Springs Art Guild, Wyoming

"AMERICAN SOUTHWEST" 19¼" x 15½" Acrylic $85.

"COASTLINE—SOUTHERN CALIFORNIA" 33" x 26½" Acrylic $225.

Shirley Lennox specializes in painting to specific order. . . landscapes, people, animals and wildlife scenes. Her goal is to capture the "feeling of the moment," and record it for others to experience.

Ms. Lennox uses various methods, including impasto techniques with additions of gravel and grasses; watercolors and also pastels with acrylics.

LENNOX, SHIRLEY A.

Lennox Art Studio
P.O. Box 405
Morton, N.Y. 14508

Summer: RD #2, Box 260
Lake George, N.Y. 12845

GALLERIES:
Adirondack Store & Gallery
  Drawer 991
  Lake Placid, N.Y. 12946
Village Gallery
  17 East Ave.
  Hilton, N.Y. 14468

EXHIBITIONS:
The Calif. Scene, Foothill
  College, Los Altos Hills, Ca.
Discovery House Gallery,
  Palo Alto, Ca.
Upstairs Gallery, Sunnyvale, Ca.
North Country Arts Center,
  Glens Falls, N.Y.
Palo Alto Art Club, Ca.
Carriage Place, Rochester, N.Y.
Lake George Inst. of History,
  Art & Science, N.Y.

AWARDS:
Bicentennial artist for Orleans
  County Centennials Corp.-1976

COLLECTIONS:
Represented in public & private
  collections across the U.S.

"FIRST DAY OUT" 14" x 18" Acrylic with Gravel $100.

LICHTENSTEIN, ROY

P.O. Box 1369
Southampton, N.Y. 11968

BORN:
New York City, Oct. 27, 1923

EXHIBITIONS:
Many 1-artist & group shows

COLLECTIONS:
Museum of Modern Art, N.Y.
Guggenheim Museum, N.Y.
Whitney Museum of Am. Art, N.Y.
Tate Gallery, London
Stedelijk Museum, Amsterdam
Pasadena Museum of Art
and many others

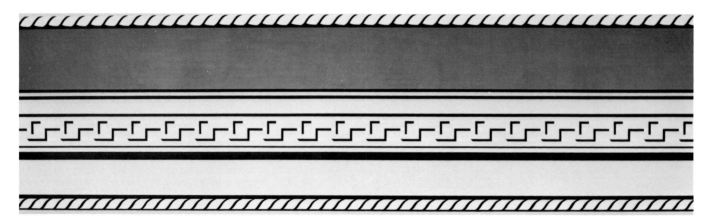

"ENTABLATURE" 1976 54" x 16" Oil & synthetic polymer paint on canvas
Collection, The Museum of Modern Art, New York
Fractional gift of an anonymous donor

LIEBERMAN, JEFFREY
405 Hendrix Street
Philadelphia, Pa. 19116

"MORNING, NEW DAWN" 14" x 18" Oil POR

LIM, KAC-KEONG K.K.
1004 Baylor Drive
Binghamton, N.Y. 13903

GALLERY:
Atlantic Gallery
1005 Thomas Jefferson St.
Washington, D.C. 20007

"FIGURES" 20" x 24" Oil NFS

EXHIBITIONS:
Roberson Center, Binghamton
Atlantic Gallery, Wash., DC
Exbtns in England, Hong
Kong, Taiwan & Brazil

AWARDS:
1st Intl. Art Exbtn, Saigon,
Diplome D'honneur
Art Society of China

COLLECTIONS:
Natl Historical Museum of
the Republic of China
Museum of the Armed Forces
of the Republic of China
Private colls. in Taiwan,
Switzerland, Hong Kong
and the U.S.

Kac-Keong Lim, a native of
China, was educated at St.
Stephan's College, Hong Kong;
Cambridge Univ; several art
schools in London; Academie
Julian, Paris and Ecole des
Beaux Arts, Geneva. He has
been the director of the Academy
of Fine Arts at Amoy, China;
Professor of Fine Arts, Polit-
ical Staff College and
concurrently Professor of Fine
Arts, College of Chinese
Culture, Taipei, Taiwan.

"COSMORAMA" 11" x 14" Oil NFS

Mr. Lim has served on screening
committees and juries in Taiwan
and has, over the years,
exhibited at the Biennial
International Exhibition of
Modern Art in Sao Paulo and has
served on its jury. He was a
member of the Committee for the
Advancement of Art in Taiwan.

LONG, MAE J.
4071 Schiller Pl.
St. Louis, Missouri 63116

"ALA SOL" 12" x 16" Acrylic POR

"PATRICIA" 12" x 16 Collage POR

LUNDIN, MARY M.
Box 2852
West Palm Beach, Fla. 33402

Summer:
RR #2, Chicaugoan Lake
Crystal Falls, Mich. 49920

COMMISSIONS:
West Palm Beach Zoo, Wall
Sculpture—"Zoo Animals"

"ZOO ANIMALS" Close-up of
large sculpture 2' x 2½' area

"ZOO ANIMALS" 7'4" x 17' Ceramic Wall Sculpture

"INNOCENCE TO SOPHISTICATION" 30" x 36" Oil

"MY ROOSTER" 32" x 36" Oil

LUNDQUIST, DOROTHY (DEA)

P.O. Box 354
Kenwood, California 95452

BORN:
Los Angeles, California

"MEMORY IS SO FAR AWAY" 18" x 22" Oil NFS

EXHIBITIONS:
Many shows, including:
Jack London Square Annual,
Oakland, Calif.
James D. Phelan Awards Show,
San Francisco, Calif.
One-artist shows in N.Y.;
San Francisco; Bangkok,
Thailand & Vientiene, Laos

AWARDS:
Best of Show & many others

COLLECTIONS:
E.M. Library, San Jose, Calif.,
Bust of Edwin Markham
Private collections in Canada,
England, Italy, India & U.S.

A surrealist and realist with a
classic technique, Dea Lundquist
does paintings in oil, egg tempera,
pastel, drawings in ink, gold-
point, silver-point and etchings.

"GOLD AND GREEN TREES" 18" x 24" Oil NFS

LUTZOW, JACK A.
240 Dolores
San Francisco, Calif. 94103

GALLERIES:
Union Art Gallery, S.F.
Perry's Gallery, S.F.

EXHIBITIONS:
Union Art Gallery, Group
Show-"Summer Exbtn."-1976-77
Perry's Gallery, S.F.

COLLECTIONS:
Numerous public & private
throughout the U.S.

"MURPHY'S TUGS" 24" x 30" Watercolor $350.

"MIGS" 3' x 4'
Oil on Canvas
NFS

MACIEL, JIM
2 John Street
New York, N.Y. 10038

GALLERY:
47 Bond St. Gallery
47 Bond St., New York, N.Y.

EXHIBITIONS:
Crapo Gallery, New Bedford
Mass., Group Show-1976
47 Bond St. Gallery, N.Y.,
One-Person Show-1977

AWARDS:
Max Beckmann Award,
Brooklyn Museum School

"MIRAGE BIBLIQUE"
27" x 7" x 5"
Plexiglas $800.

MALINAS, NICOLAS
% Ligoa Duncan "Arts"
22 E. 72nd St.
New York, N.Y. 10021

EXHIBITIONS:
Salon des Artistes Francais,
Salon d'Automne, Paris
Intl. Exbt., Karlsruhe-1977

AWARDS:
Acad. of Lutece, Silver
Andorra Intl. Exbt., 1st
Prize & Gold Medal
Intl Grand Prix, Deauville
and others

Nicolas Malinas graduated from
l'Ecole des Beaux Arts, Paris.

"COMMON EGRET"
22" x 30"
Casein Paint
$300.

MANCHESKI, MARCIA
2010 S. Williams St.
Denver, Colorado 80210

GALLERY:
Gallery 1
701 W. Hampden
Denver, Colorado

EXHIBITIONS:
Denver Audubon Soc. Annual
Wildlife Art Show, Colo.

Am. Cancer Soc., Denver
Designers' Showcase, Denver
Randi's Art Gallery, Denver
Palazzo Cenci, R.I. School
of Design, Rome, Italy

COLLECTIONS:
Private collections in
several states

"FANTASIES OF A MAN"
18" x 24"
Silkscreen
POR

MARABLE, SIMEON-DAVID de PAUL
18 Spindle Tree Rd.
Levittown, Pa. 19056

Water Street Gallery, Pa.
Gallery Upstairs

GALLERY:
Water Street Gallery
111 Water St., Bristol, Pa.

EXHIBITIONS:
One-artist shows in Albert
Lea, Minn; Mason City,
Iowa; Levittown, Pa; &
Fort Dix, N.J.

AWARDS:
Resident artist for the
Middletown Historical Soc
Nominated to Natl Soc of
Literature & the Arts by
James Michener

COLLECTIONS:
Numerous public and private

MARTINEZ, LOUIS M., Jr.
1357 W. 76th St.
Hialeah, Florida 33014

BORN:
Perris, Calif.; Jan. 30, 1951

EXHIBITIONS:
Thrice in Hortt, Ft. Lauderdale Museum, Fla.

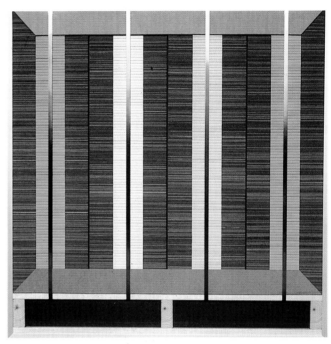

"FACADE" 42" x 42½" Mixed Medium $1,000.

MARTINELLI, SHERI
P.O. Box 1044
Pacifica, California 94044

Ezra Pound: La Martinelli Artbook: "The essence
of a religion is its art/as shows in Ursula/Lux
in Diafana/what the occident has was in Giotto/
as distinct from what we could learn from China."

"E.P. CANTO 93: LUX IN DIAFANA CREATRIX ORO" POR

"E.P. CANTO 93: URSULA BENEDETTA,
ORO" POR

MARTINEZ, YOLANDA
61 Walker Ave.
Closter, New Jersey 07624

"THE DANCERS" 43½" x 58½" Oil $1,000.

BORN:
Puerto Rico,
Dec. 16, 1951

EXHIBITIONS:
Paula Insel Gallery,
987 Third Ave., NYC

AWARDS:
Bloomfield Art League, Oils
Washington Hgts. Art Show,
N.Y., 1st prize-2 yrs.

COLLECTIONS:
Yolanda Martinez Gallery,
Closter, N.J.

Yolanda Martinez studied at
Lehman College, Fairleigh
Dickinson University, the Art
Students League and The
Ridgewood Art Association.
Her artwork has appeared in
The Inwood Heights News,
NYC. She is currently
teaching for the Washington
Heights Art Association.

"WILD FLOWERS" 18" x 24" Oil $600.

"CHILDREN"
36" x 36"
Collection, Gen.
Motors Corp.

"LAZY AFTERNOON"
Watercolor
16" x 20" $275.

MARTMER, WILLIAM P.
4356 Bundy Road
Coloma, Michigan 49038

GALLERY:
Rubiner Gallery
Washington St.
Royal Oak, Michigan

EXHIBITIONS:
Wayne Univ. Alumni Ann.

N. Ill. Univ., 1-artist
Brooklyn Museum Annual
and others

AWARDS:
Several 1st Prizes

COLLECTIONS:
Cranbrook Academy Museum
General Motors Corp.
Ford Motor Corp.

MAURER, LYDIA V.
Box 403/4th & Silver
Lake City, Colorado 81235

GALLERIES:
The Artists' Workshop
Lake City, Colo. 81235
Westside Gallery
Montrose, Colorado
Sage Dome Gallery
Hotchkiss, Colorado

Brass Cheque Gallery
Denver, Colorado
Westside Gallery, South
Ouray, Colorado

EXHIBITIONS:
Western Colo. Center for
the Arts, Grand Junction
and others

COLLECTIONS:
Many public & private

MARZEC, WANDA

62-B Glenwood Avenue
Elmwood Park, N.J. 07407

EXHIBITIONS:

Lynn Kottler Galleries, N.Y.
S. Orange & Maplewood Galleries, N.J.
Guild Mall Museum, E. Hampton, L.I.
Womanart Galleries, N.Y.
Cork Gallery, Lincoln Center, N.Y.
Manhattan Savings Bank, N.Y.
A. Styka Competition, Pa.
Atlantic City National Show
and others in U.S. & Europe

AWARDS:

A. Styke Competition, 2nd Prize
Atlantic City Natl., Honorable Ment.
Art Guild of S. Orange & Maplewood,
N.J., Members Shows, 3rd Prizes

COLLECTIONS:

Represented in public & private
collections in Poland, Canada
& the U.S.

Photographs by
D. James Dee

"LONGING" Oil

"FOGGY AFTERNOON" Oil & Acrylic

Wanda Marzec on art:
"I'm not interested in the decorative aspects of a painting. What I wish
to convey is the fate of the human being in his everyday life; his
involvement in the contemporary age; in the web of the city, commercialism,
or whatever. I do love humanity and this I wish to reflect in my work."

MAX, PETER

Peter Max Enterprises
118 Riverside Drive
New York, N.Y. 10024

BORN:

Berlin, Germany, Oct. 19, 1937

UNTITLED (BOB DYLAN)" 1967 Poster,
offset lithograph 36" x 24"
Collection, The Museum of Modern Art, New York
Gift of the designer

"TAM'S TRAIL"
14" x 18"
Oil on Canvas

McCALLA, MARY E.

264 Scenic Ridge Rd.
Kalispell, Montana 59901

GALLERY:

Ligoa Duncan "Arts"
22 E. 72nd St.
New York, N.Y. 10021

EXHIBITIONS:

Salon des Surindependants
Musee du Luxembourg
Raymond Duncan Galeries

AWARDS:

Raymond Duncan,
Prix de Paris-1977

A lover of animals and nature, Mary McCalla expresses
these feelings through the
fresh colors of the mountain
air and the shade of the
forest's cool.

McGEHEE, PAUL

4055 N. 35th St.
Arlington, Virginia 22207

BORN:
Arlington, Va., November 2, 1960

EXHIBITIONS:
Oceans Week 1978, Washington, D.C.
Hill's Art Store, one-artist show-1974
Yorktown High School Exhibitions,
    First Prize-1976, Best in Show-1978
Gallery of the Sea, Arlington, Va.-1978
Williamsburg Women's Club
Merchant Marine & Fisheries Committee
    Hearing Room, U.S. Congress, Wash., D.C.

MEMBER:
Northern Virginia Fine Arts Assoc.
American Society of Marine Artists,
    Charter Member

Paul McGehee is a self-taught artist who has
been painting in watercolors, acrylics and
oils since the age of five. In creating his
pictures, Paul utilizes information obtained
from libraries, museums and his own extensive
book and photo collection. He specializes in
landscape and marine scenes, and prefers to
work with oils on masonite.

"BOOTHBAY HARBOR, MAINE—EARLY 1930's" 20" x 24" Oil POR

ARTIST PAUL McGEHEE WITH HIS PAINTING OF HEIDELBERG, GERMANY

"U.S.R.C. 'BEAR' IN ALASKAN WATERS—1914" 30" x 40" Oil POR

"STEAMBOAT 'ST. JOHNS' ON THE POTOMAC RIVER—CIRCA 1910" 24" x 36" Oil POR

"GEORGETOWN ON THE POTOMAC RIVER" 20" x 24" Oil POR

"PASSING SCHOONERS" 20" x 24" Oil POR

McGEHEE, PAUL

"CHESAPEAKE BAY STEAMBOAT LANDING—LATE 1880's" 30" x 48" Oil POR

The steamboat "Enoch Pratt" was a familiar sight
on the Chesapeake Bay during the late 1880's. She was
named after the famous Baltimorean, and ended her days
as a barge in the years following World War I.

Limited edition prints are forthcoming.
Gallery inquiries are welcome.
Other examples of Paul McGehee's work
appeared in ARTISTS/USA 1977-78.

"STRING" 36" x 48" Oil

MASSEY, WILLIAM W., Jr.

3420-Z University Blvd., S.
Jacksonville, Fla. 32216

GALLERY:
   Gallery Vallombreuse
   Breakers Hotel
   West Palm Beach, Fla.

EXHIBITIONS:
   Nordness Gallery, N.Y.
   Coliseum Intl Art Show, N.Y.

   Ball State Univ., Muncie, In.
   Wadsworth Antheneum, Ct.
   S.E. Center for Contemporary
      Art, Winston-Salem, N.C.
   Univ. of Fla., Gainesville
   Jacksonville Univ., Fla.
   Jacksonville Art Museum, Fla

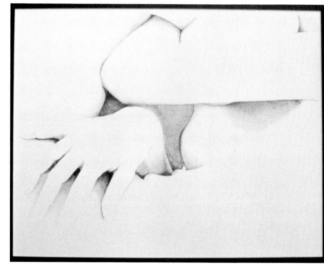

"LAURA III" 19" x 24" Pencil

McKENZIE, E.M.

4735 21st St., North
Apt. A-6
Arlington, Virginia 22207

GALLERY:
   Studio: 706 N. Glebe Rd.
   Arlington, Va. 22203

COLLECTIONS:
   Public & private collections

McMAHON, SARAN

Route 2, Box 217
Alta Loma, Texas 77510

EXHIBITIONS:
   Exbtns. throughout U.S.,
      Canada & Mexico

AWARDS:
   Over 1,500 awards

COLLECTIONS:
   Colls. throughout U.S.

Saran McMahon expresses herself in various types of art—Realist, Surrealist, Abstractionist, Landscapes, Still Life, Non-objective, Figures, (Specializing in Aspens, Seascapes and Clown Paintings), Textile Painting, Pen and Ink, Cloth and Pattern Design, China Painting, Cubist, Murals, Portraits, Tile Pictures, using watercolors, tempera, oils and many others.

"LAZY DAY IN TEXAS" Watercolor

"AND FLOWERS GROW ALL OVER THE WORLD"
Lithograph pulled on stone at Atelier Aristique
International de Seguret, Provence, France, 1977

McVEIGH, MIRIAM T.
8200 14th Street, North
St. Petersburg, Florida 33702

GALLERIES:
Chimera
St. Petersburg, Florida

Ligoa Duncan
22 E. 72nd St.
New York, N.Y. 10021

EXHIBITIONS:
Butler Inst., Youngstown, Ohio
Dayton Art Inst. Circulating Exbt.
Isaac Delgado Museum, New Orleans
American Vet. Soc. of Artists, N.Y.
St. Petersburg Jr. College, Fla.
Galerie Internationale, N.Y.
Raymond Duncan Galleries, Paris
Surindependants, Paris
Festival International de Peinture et
    Art Graphico-Plastique de St.
    Germain Des-Pres, Brussels, Belg.

AWARDS:
Hoosier Salon, Indianapolis, Ind.
Mid-Winter Suncoast Art Compet.
Festival International de Peinture et
    Art Graphico-Plastique de St.
    Germain Des-Pres, Brussels, Belg.
Legion de Honor Grand Prix
    Humanitaire de France
Order de Chevalier Associacion
    Belge-Hispanica

COLLECTIONS:
Gwen McDevitt, St. Petersburg, Fla.
Mr. R. Janseck, Orlando, Fla.
Mr. Garfield & Mr. John T. Webb,
    Ontario, Canada
Mr. Marsall Field, Sarasota, Fla.
Museum Monbart, Dijon, France
Musee des Beaux Arts de Montbard,
    Paris, France

"DANCERS" 27" x 18" Acrylic

"PAST THIS WAY" 25" x 27" Acrylic

Artist JANICE McVICAR painting "LEO AND LILLY"

McVICAR, JANICE
26180 Parkside Dr.
Hayward, California 94542

PORTRAITS: Children, Adults, Figures
Done from sittings or the artist's own
photography in her studio or the
customer's home.

"LEO AND LILLY" 20" x 24" Acrylic on Canvas NFS

MEIXNER, MARY L.
1007 Lincoln Way, Apt. 4
Ames, Iowa 50010

"UNICORN GARDEN" 27" x 37"
Acrylic & Gold Collage POR

MITCHELL, DOROTHY S.
114 Dewhurst Dr., #23A
San Antonio, Texas 78213

GALLERY:
Lynn Kottler Galleries
3 E. 65th St.
New York, N.Y. 10021

EXHIBITIONS:
Art Assn of Newport, R.I.
Mint Museum, Charlotte, NC
20th Century Gallery, Va.

Norfolk Museum, Va.
Hill Country Arts Fdn, Tex.
Texas Fine Arts Assoc.
Winston-Salem Gallery, NC
and many others

AWARDS:
Norfolk Museum, Irene
Leach Memorial Exbtn.

COLLECTIONS:
Many public & private

"RETURN TO CHINA GROVE" 16" x 20" Oil NFS

MILLER, DOROTHY DAWE
4721 Rodman St., N.W.
Washington, D.C. 20016

BORN:
New York City, Sept. 18, 1927

EXHIBITIONS:
Washington, D.C.
Rehoboth, Delaware

Dorothy Dawe Miller has received
a B.A. and M.F.A. She works in
oil, acrylic, watercolor, fiber,
plexiglas, paper collage,
tempera and encaustic.

"CARPET MOSAIC" 2' x 4'

"NEWGRANGE BURIAL" 3' x 4' Oil

"BLUE BAMBOO"
26" x 40"
Acrylic/Collage

MOCK-MORGAN, MAVERA E.
#3 Carvel Circle
Washington, D.C. 20016

EXHIBITIONS:
Art Club of Washington,
  One-artist show
American Art League
Rehoboth Art League
University of D.C.

AWARDS:
Am. Art League Award
Alaska Artists Award
Mini. Silver Sculp. Award
Who's Who in American Women

COLLECTIONS:
Cong. Robert L.F. Sikes, Fla.
Sen. Ernest Greuning, Ak.
Washington Post
Private colls. in 10 states

MORALES, ALBERT
100 Lincoln Avenue
Mineola, N.Y. 11501

BORN:
Glen Cove, N.Y.,
July 11, 1954

AWARDS:
Honorable Mention

"AFTER THE STORM" 24" x 36" Acrylic & Oil

MOORE, HENRY

℅ Marlborough Gallery
39 Old Bond St.
London, England

COLLECTIONS:
Henry Moore Sculpture Centre,
   Art Gallery of Ontario, Toronto,
   Over 300 sculptures, graphics
   and designs.
University of Chicago
Lincoln Center, N.Y.
Toledo Museum of Art
Yale Museum
and many others

"ANIMAL FORM" 1969-70 Roman travertine marble, 6'1⅝" x 8'9⅜" x 38⅝",
including separate travertine base 12" x 9'4⅛" x 53"
Collection, The Museum of Modern Art, New York.
Gift of Mr. & Mrs. Gordon Bunshaft in honor of Henry Moore.

MORFORD, JOHN A.

P.O. Box 261
Rexburg, Idaho 83440

J.Morford / Sculptor

John's unusual sensitivity to nature and the
heritage of the American West has prompted him
toward subjects that convey the subtle
relationship of man, animals and nature. He
seeks accuracy of detail, blending it with
exciting forms and textures. Each piece speaks
with the spirit of the subject, implying much
more than is stated.

"TO THE ONE LOST" 16" High Bronze
Cast at Powell Bronze Foundry, Kallispell, Montana

MORTIMER, CAROLYN G.

Commissioner's Pike
Elmer, N.J. 08318

EXHIBITIONS:
DuPont Country Club Art
   Gall., Del., 1-artist
   and group shows
Cape May Art League, N.J.
Soc. of N.J. Artists
   Exbtn, Atlantic City

Ocean City Cultural Arts
   Center, N.J.
Ware Gallery, Ardentown
Peoples Bank of Woodstown,
   N.J., 1-artist shows
Photographic Soc. of Phila.
Wheaton Village Museum, N.J.

AWARDS:
Many top awards

COLLECTIONS:
Numerous public & private

"BLUE MARSH" 20" x 30" Oil POR

MOULTRIE, JAMES
131 Governors Road
Lakewood, N.J. 08701

GALLERIES:
Mini-Gallery
131 Governors Road
Lakewood, N.J. 08701
Studio II
458 W. 151st, N.Y.C. 10031

"OUT IN THE OPEN" 11" x 14"
Ball Point Pen NFS

EXHIBITIONS:
Atlantic City Outdoor Show
Lakewood Arts & Crafts
Allied Artists of America
Rego Park Outdoor Show
Studio II Gallery
One-artist shows:
Mini-Gallery, N.J.
Beacon Manor, N.J.

AWARDS:
Many top awards

COLLECTIONS:
Bureau of Cartooning,
Colorado Springs, Colo.

Jim Moultrie works as a free-lance illustrator, doing portrait commissions, selling paintings and marketing his own prints. He trained under the late artist/illustrator Frank J. Reilly at the Art Students' League, The Frank J. Reilly School of Art in New York City. Later, he studied at and graduated from The Albert Pels School of Art, also in New York City. His style is realistic in the traditional manner, executing his works in oils, acrylics, watercolors, pastel pencils and pen and ink.

"WHITE FEATHER" 24" x 34"
Acrylic on Canvas NFS

MOTHERWELL, ROBERT
909 North St.
Greenwich, Connecticut 06830

BORN:
Aberdeen, Wash., Jan. 24, 1915

GALLERY:
David Mirvish Gallery
596 Markham St.
Toronto, Ontario, Canada

"GAULOISES BLEUES (RAW UMBER EDGE)" 1971
Aquatint and line cut printed in very light blue,
vivid purple blue and light olive brown,
plate: 11⅝" x 6 ⁹/₁₆", sheet: 22 ¹⁵/₁₆" x 15½"
Collection, The Museum of Modern Art, New York
Gift of Celeste Bartos

"ENCHANTMENT" 24" x 30" Lithograph POR

MUSGRAVE, REAL
3611 Marsh Lane Place
Dallas, Texas 75220

GALLERY:
Mandala Art Gallery
6617 Snider Plaza
Dallas, Texas 75205

EXHIBITIONS:
"Fantasy Art" Shows,
1 & 2-artist shows

Many shows in sculpture,
printmaking, painting
and drawing

COLLECTIONS:
Public & private in U.S.,
Great Britain, France,
Guatemala & So. Africa

MURPHY, MARIE L.
4949 Battery Lane
Bethesda, Maryland 20014

GALLERY:
Art Contemporary
4948 St. Elmo Blvd.
Bethesda, Maryland 20014

EXHIBITIONS:
Washington Gallery of Art,
    Several one-artist shows
Print Gallery of Georgetown,
    Drawings & Watercolors showings
Group shows locally and in Florida,
    N.Y. and Massachusetts

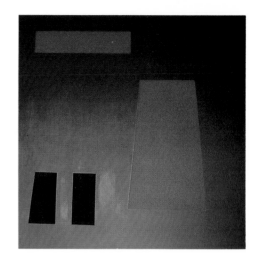

"PERUVIAN XI" 44" x 44" Acrylic POR

"DIALOG XII" 36" x 36" Acrylic POR

"TULA V" 31" x 46" Acrylic POR

"TOLTEC X" 46" x 46" Acrylic POR

Marie Murphy studied at Corcoran Art School
and with individual art teachers. She has
been admitted to practice law in Massachusetts
and has several books of poetry outstanding.
Her art is included in many private
collections.

MUSIAL, ANDREW
41-B Linwood Avenue
Elmwood Park, N.J. 07407

EXHIBITIONS:
Lynn Kottler Galleries, N.Y.
S. Orange & Maplewood Galleries, N.J.
Guild Mall Museum, E. Hampton, L.I.
A. Styka Competition, Pa.
Maplewood Memorial Library, N.J.
and others in U.S. & Europe

AWARDS:
A. Styka Competition, 1st Prize
Atlantic City Arts & Crafts Show
S. Orange & Maplewood Gallery, 1st Prize
and other top awards in U.S. & Europe

COLLECTIONS:
Public & private collections in Poland,
Canada, Spain & the U.S.

Andrew Musial's views on art:
"In my work, the subject matter, either
architecture, landscapes, human forms or
animals, is presented synthetically only
to stimulate the imagination. When
working, the canvas at times absorbs me
magically into itself in such a fashion
that I don't foresee the final results.
This in itself is an aesthetic experience
and a revelation."

Photographs by D. James Dee

"GREAT NUDE" Oil & Acrylic

"LANDSCAPE WITH SUN" Oil

NAKACHE, MARGARET
1448 Woodacre Drive
McLean, Virginia 22101

EXHIBITIONS:
Annual in Paris and major U.S. cities

COLLECTIONS:
Represented in private and public
collections in Africa, the Americas,
Europe and Asia

Margaret Nakache received her education from
the Rhode Island School of Design and Beaux-Arts
in Paris.

"EAST OF ST. TROPEZ" 22" x 28" Watercolor POR

NAOMI, JILL
405 Hendrix St.
Philadelphia, Pa. 19116

EXHIBITIONS:
Gimbels Art Exhibit,
Phila., 1975, 76

"MORE THAN A DOG" Pen & Ink POR

The artist in his studio

NADALINI, LOUIS E.
154 Lynn Street
Seattle, Washington 98109

BORN:
San Francisco, Ca., Jan. 21, 1927

COLLECTIONS:
Oakland Art Museum, Calif.
Univ. of Calif. at Berkeley
San Francisco Public Schools
Wells Fargo Bank, S.F.
U.S. Public Health Hospital, Seattle
and many other public & private
collections in Europe & the U.S.

GALLERY:
La Galerie Mouffe
67 rue Mouffetard
75005 Paris, France

EXHIBITIONS:
Pa. Academy of Art, Phila.
Whitney Museum Annual, N.Y.
Calif. Palace of Legion of Honor
S.F. Museum of Art Annual, Calif.
Oakland Art Museum Annual
M.H. De-Young Memorial Museum, S.F.
Western Museum Travelling Juried Exbt.
La Galerie Mouffe, Paris, France
Esther Baer Gallery, Santa Barbara
Haggin Gallery, Berkeley, Calif.
Brickwall Gallery, Berkeley, Calif.
Cellini Gallery, San Francisco
Kaiser Center Art Gallery, Oakland
Gallery A, Taos, N.M.
Los Angeles Art Assoc. Galleries
And/Or Gallery, Northwest Projects,
    Seattle, Washington
Gordon Woodside Galleries, Seattle
Salon Intl., Biarritz, France
San Francisco Art Commission
San Francisco Public Library,
    Travelling Exbtn.
Atlantic City Art Center, N.J.
James Gallery, N.Y.
San Francisco Art Inst., Calif.
20 one-artist shows throughout the
    world, including:
    Village Art Center, N.Y.
    Am. Students & Artists Center,
        Paris, France
    Lucien Labaudt Gallery, S.F.
    Arleigh Gallery, S.F.
    Univ. of Calif. at Berkeley
    El-Crito Gallery, Venezuela
    L'Envoi Gallery, S.F.
    Coffee Gallery, S.F.
    Galerie Vallombreuse, Biarritz, Fr.
    Gordon Woodside Galleries, Seattle
and many other natl & regl shows

AWARDS:
YMCA All City Art Exbtn, 1st Prize
James D. Phelan Award, Palace
    Legion of Honor
Merit of Awards in Art, London, Eng.
Salon International, Diplome
    D'Honneur, France

Louis Nadalini studied art at the City College of San Francisco, the Art Students League in New York with George Grosz and also studied in San Francisco with Martin Baer. Preferring to work in oils, acrylics and ink, Mr. Nadalini is listed in *Who's Who in American Art, Who's Who in the West, Who's Who in America* (39th edition-1977) and *Dictionary of International Biography*, England.

According to Nadalini:
    "New ideas by their very nature require new language—they cannot be expressed in any other way.
    "The supreme misfortune is when theory outstrips performance.
    "The painter's business is to practice art, not to talk about it."

"MARY JANE, THE ALL-AMERICAN GIRL" 50" x 68" Oil

ARTISTS/USA

"THE AQUEAN ANGLE" Lithograph $200.

NARDONE, VINCENT J.
75 Essex Avenue
Maplewood, New Jersey 07040

℅ Ligoa Duncan Gallery
22 E. 72nd St., New York, N.Y. 10021

GALLERIES:
  Ligoa Duncan Gallery, N.Y.
  Galeries Raymond Duncan, Paris
  Whistler's Daughter, Baskins Ridge, N.J.
  Duncan-Echeverria Gallery, Beach Haven, N.J.
  Innovative Interiors, Livingston, N.J.
  The Connoisseur, Ltd., Ocean City, N.J.

EXHIBITIONS:
  University of Southern California
  Columbian Foundation, N.J.
  Galeries Raymond Duncan, Paris
  International Art Festival, Paris
  Whitney Counterweight, N.Y.
  Scripps College, Calif.
  American Painters in Paris
  Ligoa Duncan Gallery, N.Y.
  Salon des Artistes Francais, Paris
  Artistes U.S.A., Paris
  Academie Internationale de Lutece, Paris

AWARDS:
  Atlantic City National Show
  Art Centre of the Oranges, N.J.
  South Orange State Outdoor Show, N.J.
  Art Guild of South Orange & Maplewood, N.J.
  N.J. State Council on the Arts, N.J.
  Art at the Mall State Show, N.J.
  Prix de Paris, Raymond Duncan, Paris
  and many others

Born in South Orange, N.J., Vincent Nardone received a B.A. from Montclair State College and an M.F.A. from the University of Southern California. He also studied in Paris at the Paris American Academy des Beaux Arts. Mr. Nardone is listed in the 1978 edition of *Who's Who in American Art* and his artwork has been reviewed in *Peintres Americans* by Robert Urinat, *La Revue Moderne* by Renee Carvalito, *N.J. Music and Arts Magazine, Matzner Publications* of N.J., *Carrefour* by Denis Roger, *Suburban N.J. Life Magazine* and the *News Record of Maplewood and South Orange*, N.J.

Vincent Nardone as the artist has attributed his deep involvement with teaching art to children; a turning point in his art—working with children makes his imagination flow towards a kind of playfulness, a creative urge that puts down his ideas so that we can ponder visually.

COLLECTIONS:
  Tuscan School, Maplewood
  Ligoa Duncan Gallery, N.Y.
  Hall of Records, Newark
  Univ. of So. California
  M.G.M. Studios, Calif.
  Rome Daily Am. News, Italy
  Creative Educ. Fdn., N.Y.
  Newark Museum, N.J.
  Christ the King Parish,
    Sardenia
  Music & Arts Corp. of N.J.
  Raymond Duncan Museum, Paris
  Newark Public Library, N.J.
  Bonanza Restaurant chain

  Mr. & Mrs. Gil Michalsky
  Van Cliburn
  Dr. & Mrs. Justice Schiffers
  Allan Samson
  Hank Budnick
  Mr. & Mrs. Frank Politano
  Mr. & Mrs. E.J. Scrofani
  Woody Herman
  Mr. & Mrs. Joseph Bayer
  Dr. J.P. Guilford
  Mary Mateer
  Mr. & Mrs. N. Spagnoletti
  Mr. & Mrs. Michael Decicco
  Dr. & Mrs. Donald Lombardi
  Dr. & Mrs. Stephen Vanna

"SAND DUNES" Lithograph $200.

"QUINTET" Woodcut $100.

NARIKAWA, SHIGERU S.N.

6 Jones St., #4B
New York, N.Y. 10014

BORN:
Japan, May 30, 1946

EXHIBITIONS:
National Print Exbtn/Potsdam Prints
Hawaii National Print Exbtn.
Honolulu Printmakers Exbtn.
New Directions in Printmaking,
   Pratt Graphics Center Traveling Show
Art Hawaii, Honolulu Academy of Arts
4 one-artist shows, Honolulu, Hawaii

AWARDS:
The State Foundation on Culture and
   the Arts, Hawaii, Purchase
   Awards-1971, 73 & 77
City & County of Honolulu,
   Artistic Achievement Award-1972,
   Purchase Award-1975
Contemporary Arts Center of Hawaii,
   Purchase Award-1976

COLLECTIONS:
Honolulu Academy of Arts
The State Foundation on Culture
   and the Arts
City and County of Honolulu
Contemporary Arts Center of Hawaii
World Print Competition, S.F., Calif.

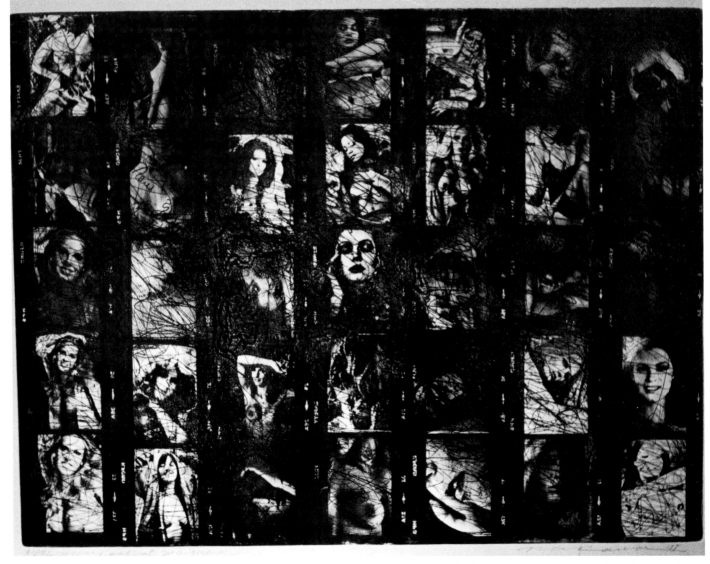

"MEN LOOK AT WOMEN" 24" x 32" Etching $200.

NEBEL, KARL
166-25 Powells Cove Blvd., Apt. 20 L
Beechhurst, N.Y. 11357

An American artist living in New York—

likes photography—

does not like photographic painting—

tries to create (rather

than describe) life on a canvas—

loves colors on their

own terms—answers (rather than apes)

reality—finds magic in

a spray gun—considers the canvas a

flat, two-dimensional

object (to become friends with a wall)—

flirts (at the same time)

with a third dimension—and does not

worry his head off

what anybody else might have to say—

"MEMORIAL TO THE GUARD" 37" x 78"
Acrylic on Canvas POR

NASRI, GERTRUD
1230 SE Morrison, #403
Portland, Oregon 97214

AGENT:
Caroline Johnson
Route 4, Box 1174
Gresham, Oregon 97030

BORN:
St. Paul, Minnesota

Gertrud Nasri does portraits and compositions, using oils, acrylics and mixed media. A color brochure is available from the artist. She is a member of Artists Equity, Washington, D.C.

"THE LIONS, for Sonja" Charcoal on Paper 18" x 24" NFS
Also: Oil on Masonite 22" x 28" POR

NEVELSON, LOUISE
29 Spring Street
New York, N.Y. 10012

BORN:
Kiev, Russia, 1900

EXHIBITIONS:
One-artist & group shows throughout the world

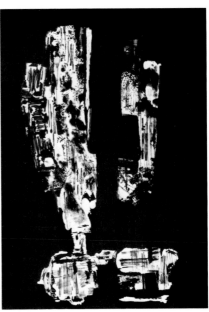

"UNTITLED" 1963 Lithograph, printed in deep blue and black
comp. and sheet: 33⅛" x 23⅛"
Collection, The Museum of Modern Art, New York
Gift of Kleiner, Bell & Co.

OLDENBURG, CLAES
℅ Petersburg Press
18 E. 81st St.
New York, N.Y. 10028

BORN:
Stockholm, Sweden, Jan. 28, 1929

EXHIBITIONS:
Metropolitan Museum of Art, N.Y.
Philadelphia Museum of Art
Many other one-artist & group shows

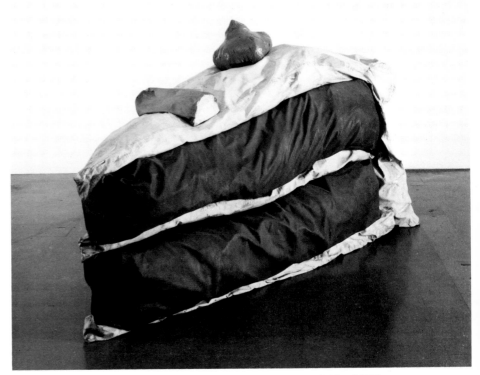

"FLOOR CAKE (GIANT PIECE OF CAKE)" 1962 58⅜" x 9'6¼" x 58⅜"
Synthetic polymer paint and latex on canvas filled with foam rubber and cardboard
Collection, The Museum of Modern Art, New York
Gift of Philip Johnson

"VIEW OF MILAN" 16" x 20" Black Ink Drawing $100.

OILAR, JOHN R.
813 S. 10th St.
Lafayette, Indiana 47905

BORN:
Lafayette, Indiana,
January 22, 1949

EXHIBITIONS:
Lafayette Art Center
McCray Art Gallery,
Western N.M. Univ.
Several in Minneapolis

AWARDS:
Professional Best
and many others

COLLECTIONS:
Several public & private
throughout West &
Midwest

PANGALOS, MARIA
159–00 Riverside Dr., W.
New York, N.Y. 10032

GALLERY:
Ligoa Duncan
22 E. 72nd St., N.Y.C.

EXHIBITIONS:
NYIAS, New York-1970
Ligoa Duncan, 1970–77
Salon 50 States, 1973–78
Musee Lougemburg, Paris
Grand Salon, 1976
Soc. des Artiste Francais

Maliotis Cultural Center,
Brookline, Mass.

AWARDS:
Pris de Paris
Grand Prix Humanitaire
of France
Palme d'or Prom Queen
Fabiola of Belgium and
Cross of Chevalier
Gold Medal, C.H.R. Rep.
Dominicana and Est.
Unitos Mexicanos
and many others

"PASTORALE WITH OLIVE TREES"
24" x 30" Acrylic $1,200.

PARDO, LYNN
12065 Edgewater Drive
Lakewood, Ohio 44107

EXHIBITIONS:
Estate of the Arts,
Cleveland, Ohio
Cleveland Home & Flower Show
Cleveland State Univ.,
Student Exhibition
Many other regional shows

AWARDS:
Outstanding in Show and
many others

COLLECTIONS:
Private collections in
Ohio, Calif., Pa. & Ariz.

PARTIDA, ELENA
3691 N.E. 15th Ave.
Pompano Beach, Fla. 33064

BORN:
Chicago, Illinois, 1905

EXHIBITIONS:
Chicago, Ill., 3 1-artist
Partida Gallery of Art,
Southampton, L.I., N.Y.

Ft. Lauderdale, Fla.
New York City
Norton Gallery, Palm Beach
Easthampton Guild, L.I.

COLLECTIONS:
Brooklyn Children's Museum
Brooklyn Museum, N.Y.
Private colls. in Chicago,
N.Y., L.I. & Fla.

"BACK PORCH" 24" x 28" Acrylic POR

"THE MOVING TIDE" 1960 48" x 96" Textured Oil POR

PIPER, MAL

1823 Woodside Drive
Arlington, Texas 76013

BORN:
Macon, Georgia; Feb., 1924

COLLECTIONS:
Australian Spitfire Assoc., Sydney
American Airlines Museum, Tulsa
U.S. Air Force Academy
Congressman Jim Wright, Wash., D.C.
Private collections

"TIGER" 15" x 22" Watercolor NFS

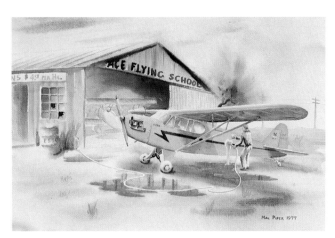

"THE SUMMER OF '41" 14" x 21" Watercolor
Limited Edition Print of 1,000—Signed $20.

"PACIFIC B-24" 21" x 28" Watercolor
Limited Edition Print of 950—Signed $25.

"WAXAHACHIE HOUSE" 22" x 29" Watercolor
Limited Edition Print of 295—Signed $40.

Mal Piper learned to fly in the RCAF in 1941, transferring to the U.S. Air Corps where he was a combat pilot in World War II. He studied architecture at the University of Sydney, Australia and returned to flying in 1948 with Australian National Airways. He is now a Captain for a major U.S. airline.

Mal Piper works only in traditional watercolor and does paintings of aircraft and air combat scenes on request.

"EAGLES WORLD" 30" x 40" Oil on Canvas $5,000.

POHOLE, FRANK A.

753 39th Street
Brooklyn, N.Y. 11232

GALLERY:
Minerva Art Gallery
250 E. 58th St.
New York, N.Y. 10022

BORN:
Trieste, Italy; Sept. 8, 1920

EXHIBITIONS:
Yearly one-artist shows:
Asociacion Estimulo de
Bellas Artes, Buenos
Aires, 1954-62

Galeria Libertad, Buenos
Aires, 1953-62
Galeria Renoir, Buenos
Aires, 1953-62
Municipal Exbtns, Buenos
Aires, 1954-62
Minerva Art Gallery,
N.Y., 1977-78

COLLECTIONS:
Numerous public & private
throughout Argentina,
So. America, Canada,
Europe & U.S.

Frank Pohole is one of the few select artists in the world whose proven capacity to paint strictly with his fingers puts him in a class by himself. The consequence of his worldwide artistic travels makes him an exceptionally rare linguist who speaks sixteen different languages.

Educated in Europe, Pohole received a degree in International Sciences from the University of Buenos Aires in 1961. He once worked as an interpreter for the criminal court of the City of New York.

"THUNDERSTORM" 30" x 40" Oil on Canvas $4,000.

"WHITE HORSE" 24" x 30" Oil on Canvas $6,000.

"NATURE AT NOON" 30" x 36" Oil on Canvas $3,000.

PEER, PAULA E.
Box 502
Blue Hill, Maine 04614

BORN:
United Kingdom,
Sept. 4, 1915

GALLERY:
Sunbury Mall
Central St., Bangor, Me.

EXHIBITIONS:
American Embassy, Mexico
Bar Harbor Bank,
Permanent exhibit
Santiago, Chile
Vientiane, Laos, USIS
and local exhibits

COLLECTIONS:
Private in U.S. & abroad

"RHYTHM" 36" x 48" Acrylic $400.

POLLEY, EDGAR L.
1806 Beachwood Ave.
New Albany, Ind. 47150

GALLERIES:
Little Gallery
1622 Story Ave.
Louisville, Ky.
Colonial Frame Shoppe
2015 E. Spring
New Albany, Indiana

AWARDS:
Paier School of Art, New
Haven, Ct., Hon. Mention
Fourth of July Art Festival,
New Albany, Indiana,
Honorable Mention

COLLECTIONS:
Original Artist Brokerage
Co., Louisville, Ky.

Edgar Polley is a member of
The International Society
of Artists, N.Y.

"A STUDY OF TURNIPS" 15¾" x 20¼" Acrylic $92.

PRENTISS, TINA
Wilmington, Mass. 01887

GALLERY:
OUI, Inc., 54 Canal St.
Boston, Mass. 02114

EXHIBITIONS:
Intl Women's Year Exbt.,
Royal Society of Art,
Adelaide, Australia-1975
Boston Museum of Fine Arts
Busch-Reisinger Museum
Attleboro Museum
15 one-artist shows, 110
others-US & 5 countries

AWARDS:
Creative Painting, Several
national prizes
SPCA Bronze Medal
Grumbacher Award
and others

COLLECTIONS:
Smithsonian Inst., Wash.,
DC, Archives of Am. Art
Museum Contemp. Crafts, NY,
Research & Educ. Dept.
Many private collections

"LOUISE NEVELSON WALL SCULPTURE ON CITY
HALL PLAZA, BOSTON" ©1972 24" x 36" Acrylic

"EARLY MORNING"
Oil on Canvas
30" x 40" POR

PURDY, ROBERT CLEAVER
851 Lexington Ave.
New York, N.Y. 10021

GALLERY:
Lynn Kottler Gallery
3 E. 65th St.
New York, N.Y. 10022

EXHIBITIONS:
Feragil Galleries,
5 one-artist shows
Tasca Galleries

AWARDS:
4 Louis Comfort Tiffany
Fellowships

COLLECTIONS:
Metropolitan Museum, N.Y.
Chicago Art Institute
Pa. Academy of Art
Brooklyn Museum of Art
and many others

PRAZEN, GARY F.

Box 146N, Rt. 1
Helper, Utah 84526

GALLERY:
Gary Prazen Gallery
Box 146N, Rt. 1
Helper, Utah 84526

EXHIBITIONS:
World Shows: Las Vegas, Nevada
World Shows: Denver, Colorado
I.S.A. Shows, Salt Lake City, Utah
Television Exhibition
Gary Prazen Gallery
Zions First National Bank
Royal Inns Hotel, Salt Lake City
Walker Bank
Several one-artist shows

AWARDS:
North American Artists, Denver, Colo.,
  Gold Medallion: Best in Show Award
Numerous blue ribbons

COLLECTIONS:
Pacific First Federal Savings Bank,
  Spokane, Wash., 30' metal wall murals
  depicting Spokane history

Gary Prazen teaches metal arts at the
College of Eastern Utah. He does metal
sculptured wall murals, metal full
dimension sculptures, stone sculptures,
wood and fiberglass sculptures and
blacksmith art.

"BULL ELK" 1977 8' Steel & Epoxy
Collection of Price Elks Lodge, Price, Utah

"DRAGON" 1978 37" $3,500.
Steel wire welded. Mounted on lava, copper & brass

"WE WILL FIGHT NO MORE FOREVER" 1978 25" $500.
Marble with steel, copper & brass trim

RANDLETT, STUART E.
Box 483, Menwith Hill Sta.
APO N.Y. 09210

EXHIBITIONS:
  House of Delegates,
    Annapolis, Md.
  Capitol Center Gallery,
    Landover, Md.
  Congress, Wash., D.C.
  Montpelier Mansion,
    Laurel, Md.
  Norfolk, Va.
  London, England
  Harrogate, England

AWARDS:
  Numerous in Va. & Md. shows

COLLECTIONS:
  Numerous private collections
    In U.S. & Great Britain

"WEST TANFIELD IN NORTH YORKSHIRE"

Stuart Randlett was born in Richmond, Va. and studied privately in
Norfolk, Va. He later took the Famous Artists correspondence course
and studied watercolor for several years with William "Skip" Lawrence
in Maryland and with Edgar Whitney and Carl Schmalz. He is currently
residing in Harrogate, England and is concentrating on painting the
North of England in watercolor. He is a member of the Baltimore Watercolor
Society and the Doncaster Art Club in England.

"NORTHUMBERLAND CASTLE"

RANDALL, PAULA

441 Ramona Ave.
Sierra Madre, Ca. 91024

BORN:
Minnesota, Dec. 21, 1895

EXHIBITIONS:
Galerie Vallombreuse, Fr.
Frank Lang Gallery, L.A.
University of Taiwan
Pasadena Art Museum, Ca.

AWARDS:
Laguna Beach Art Museum,
First Award
Pasadena Soc. of Artists
All California Exbt.

COLLECTIONS:
Natl Audubon Soc., Western
Div., Sacramento, Ca.
Pasadena Tournam. of Roses
City of Hope, Ca.
Eva Gabor, Hollywood, Ca.

"THE LITTLE WHEELS AND THE BIG WHEELS"
Cast Aluminum $1,250.

REINEL, ROLAND

"The Citadel"
P.O. Box 325
Stuart, Florida 33494

COLLECTIONS:
Many public & private
in U.S. & Europe

"LE TAUREAU DOMPTE" 1977   4⅛' x 5½'   Oil

RAVOIRA, JAMES

138 Bull Street
Charleston, South Carolina 29401

GALLERY:
Lynn Kottler Galleries
65th St. betw. Madison & 5th Ave.
New York, N.Y.

EXHIBITIONS:
Lynn Kottler Galleries, N.Y.,-
1977 & 78
Myrtle Beach Convention Center, S.C.

AWARDS:
Eleanor G. Caldwell Award,
Bethany, West Virginia

James Ravoira received a B.A. from
West Liberty State College in West
Virginia, an M.A. from Kent State
University in Ohio and an M.F.A.
from Kent State. He is listed in
*Who's Who in the South and Southwest-
1978.*

"THE EXPERIMENT" 45" x 51" Acrylic $7,000.

RAUSCHENBERG, ROBERT

381 Lafayette St.
New York, N.Y. 10003

BORN:
Port Arthur, Texas, Oct. 22, 1925

EXHIBITIONS:
Many group & one-artist shows in
U.S. & abroad

COLLECTIONS:
Albright-Knox Gallery, Buffalo
Whitney Museum of Am. Art, N.Y.
White Museum, Cornell University
Tate Gallery, London
Goucher College
and many others

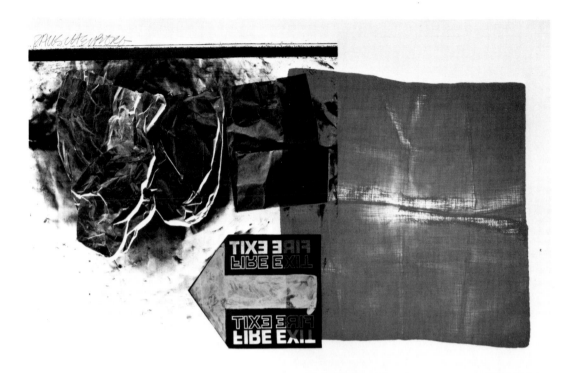

"TREATY" 1974 Lithograph, printed in black, black brown, deep orange red,
black red, pale purple blue, dark blue and yellow gray, on two sheets,
sheet (both) 54⅛" x 40 ³/₁₆", comp. (both): 47⅜" x 40¼"
Collection, The Museum of Modern Art, New York
Gift of Celeste Bartos

REEVES, BETTY-JOY (MRS. ROSSER)
24 Gramercy Park
New York, N.Y. 10003

STUDIO:
National Arts Club
15 Gramercy Park
New York, N.Y. 10003

EXHIBITIONS:
National Arts Club,
5 juried shows
Beaux Arts Annual, Richmond
Moscow, USSR, Portraits USA/
USSR Chess Teams
Salsjobaden, Sweden
Womanart Gallery, N.Y.
Pastel Society, Rockport
& Gloucester, Mass.
and many others

AWARDS:
Various top awards

COLLECTIONS:
Manhattan Chess Club
Smith College
and many private collections
in 6 states, Jamaica
and Bermuda

"GAUCHO" 18" x 28" Oil on Canvas $600.

"MICHELLE, FASHION DECREES...THE LOOSE
LOOK" 18" x 24" Oil on Canvas $500.

Betty-Joy Reeves illustrated
The Brides Book for Holt,
Rhinehart and did many illustrations and cartoons for magazines and childrens books. These
were always signed, "Betty-Joy
Street" or "B. Joy Street." Now
after a lapse for a busy and
rewarding life with children, a
husband's career and much travel,
she has resumed her first and
abiding love—painting and sculpting
people in their own special world.

RIZZO

GALLERY:
Joy Rubin Art Gallery
101 Hollywood Fashion Center
Hollywood, Florida 33023

Untitled 6" Hydrocal NFS

"LANDSCAPE 2" 24" x 36" Acrylics POR

"NOBSKA LIGHT, WOODS HOLE, CAPE COD" 19" x 32" Watercolor NFS

RINALDO, KAREN A.

29 Great Bay Road
Teaticket, Mass. 02536

GALLERIES:
Cape Cod Art Association
Route 6A
Barnstable, Mass.

Falmouth Artists' Guild
Main St., Falmouth, Mass.

EXHIBITIONS:
Ortins, Falmouth, Mass.
Harbor View, Falmouth
New England Gallery of Art,
Chatham, Mass.
Uncle Bill's Country Store,
North Falmouth, Mass.

AWARDS:
Cape Cod Art Association, Special Award,
Design and Illustration
Georgia-Pacific Corp. of N.Y.,
Graphic Arts Excellence
Falmouth Career Women's Award, 1976
National Federation of Business and
Professional Women's Clubs,
Certificate of Merit, 1976

COLLECTIONS:
Falmouth Town Hall, 76' mural
Falmouth Nurses Assoc., 21' mural
Barnstable County National Bank
Cape Cod Writers Conference
Cape Cod Town Halls and
Historical Societies
Olde Colonial Courthouse, Barnstable
Cornell Fine Arts Center,
Rollins College, Florida
President's Office, Rollins College
and many others in U.S. and abroad

"S.S. NOBSKA, WOODS HOLE, CAPE COD"
27" x 35" Watercolor Private Collection

"BRIDGE OVER OTTAUQUECHEE RIVER, WOODSTOCK, VERMONT"
27" x 35" Watercolor Private Collection

Karen A. Rinaldo studied at the
Worcester Art Museum and at the
Conservatory of Music and Arts in
Barnstable. Within the past three
years, thirteen of her watercolor
paintings have been reproduced as
prints, totalling 19,000 limited
edition full-color reproductions.
A study of Japanese art and culture
was combined on a visit to Japan in
1977.

For her contribution to
Bicentennial art, Ms. Rinaldo
received correspondence from
Pres. Gerald R. Ford, Sen. Edward
Kennedy, John W. Warner, Hon. James
Hanley, Norman Rockwell and
Gov. Michael S. Dukakis of Massachusetts. Recognition of this work
was given her on WTEV-TV. She is
listed in ARTISTS/USA 1977-78 and
in the Bicentennial Edition.

RIVERS, LARRY
92 Little Plains Road
Southampton, N.Y. 11968

BORN:
New York, N.Y., 1923

GALLERY:
Marlborough Gallery, Inc.
41 E. 57th St.
New York, N.Y. 10022

Larry Rivers studied at the Hans
Hofmann School of Fine Arts and
New York University.

"DIANA WITH POEM" 1970-74
Three dimensional lithograph with poem by Kenneth Koch,
four sheets: 16¾" x 19¼"
Collection, The Museum of Modern Art, New York
Gift of Celeste Bartos

ROSENBERG, YETTA
16605 Aldersyde Drive
Shaker Hts., Ohio 44120

GALLERY:
Malvina Freedson Gallery
12700 Lake Avenue
Cleveland, Ohio 44107

EXHIBITIONS:
Women's City Club, Cleve.
Patterson Gallery, N.Y.
Mather Gallery, Cleveland
Cleveland Museum, Ohio
and many others

COLLECTIONS:
Many private collections

"THE FLAME" 12' high Bronze NFS

SAULE, VIGEO
425 Riverside Drive
New York, N.Y. 10025

GALLERY:
Raymond Duncan Galeries
31 rue de Seine
75006 Paris, France

EXHIBITIONS:
Academie Internationale de
Lutece, Paris-1978
Salon des Surindependants,
Musee du Luxembourg,
Paris-1979
1-artist & juried shows in
U.S., Venezuela, Mexico,
Canada, Germany & France

"WATCH OUT!" 24" x 18" Watercolor POR

SALLÈ, JACQUES
365 Seventh Ave.
New York, N.Y. 10001

BORN:
Lisbon, Portugal, 1949

GALLERY:
N.Y. Art Tribe

EXHIBITIONS:
"Black & White" the Spike,
N.Y.C.

"WAITING LINE N.Y.?" 1978 60" x 60" POR

"DISC PEOPLE" 1977 50" x 105" POR

SCHAUER, WALBURGA "WALLY"

218 Avenida Rosa #1
San Clemente, Calif. 92672

GALLERY:
Quorum Gallery
354 N. Coast Hwy.
Laguna Beach, Calif. 92651

EXHIBITIONS:
Fiesta de Artes, La Mirada
Orange County Fair

Hillcrest Annual Festival
San Clemente Arts & Crafts
Art-A-Fair, Laguna Beach
Laguna Fed. Savings & Loan

AWARDS:
Numerous top awards

COLLECTIONS:
Museum-Gallery, Argentina
Private collections in Europe
& throughout U.S.

"YUCCA" 30" x 30" Acrylic $300.

SCHEFFLER, FRAN

Studio and Gallery
4344A Seagrape Drive
Lauderdale-By-The-Sea, Florida 33308

"OLYMPIA FOREST" 24" x 35" Oil $500.

SCHIMPF, RUTH 'ENGLISH'

2154 W. Spring St.
Lima, Ohio 45805

GALLERIES:
Gallery A, Taos, N.M.
Le Monde, Dayton, Ohio

EXHIBITIONS:
Allen County Historical
Society, Lima, Ohio
Many 1-artist & group shows

COLLECTIONS:
Represented in numerous
public & private colls.

Ruth Schimpf's works include
architecture, scenery and
studies of people, but birds
and flowers are her
specialty. She signs her
works "English."

"BAY-BREASTED WARBLER" 8" x 10" Acrylic POR

SHAFFETT, RICHARD, Jr.

956 Pomelo Avenue
Sarasota, Florida 33579

GALLERIES:
Forms in Sculpture Gallery,
Sarasota, Florida
Schoolhouse Gallery,
Sanibel Island, Florida

"EGRET" 40" wide x 38" high $600.
Redwood with metal legs, claw & base
Painted with gesso & acrylics

SHAPIRO, DAVID S.

RD 1, Box 51A Hall Rd.
Friendsville, Pa. 18818

David Shapiro is an assistant professor of painting and drawing at SUNY, Binghamton. He is director of visual arts for the Easy Motion Institute for Creativity Research, N.Y.

AWARDS:

American Academy in Rome, "Prix de Rome"-Painting
SUNY Research Grant

"STILL LIFE
IN RED"
48" x 36"
$6,000.

"MORNING VISITORS" 54" x 64" Oil POR

SHECTER, MARK

1800 N. Charles St.
Baltimore, Maryland 21201

EXHIBITIONS:

U.S. Embassies worldwide
Intl. Art Show, N.Y.
Johns Hopkins University
American Film Institute
Chrysler Museum

COLLECTIONS:

Corcoran Gallery of Art
Hebrew Union College Mus'm
Washington Cnty Museum
Lowe Art Center, Syracuse
Jewish Hist. Soc. of Md.
St. Joseph Hosp., Balt.
Har Sinai Temple, Balt.
Beth Tfiloh Synagogue
Lady Epstein Coll., London
Johnny Carson, Calif.
and 42 private collections

There are two major themes in the work of Ilya Shenker—one Russian and the other Jewish—which entwine and complement each other beautifully. They provide an echo of both Russian and Jewish folklore. The artist's emotions toward the cherished treasures of Jewish culture which are now dying under Soviet conditions depict an equally profound feeling of grief. In Ilya Shenker's paintings, that which is dying comes alive, at times with lyrical warmth and at other moments with tender irony.

"MUSICIANS" 30" x 20" Acrylic $1,300.

"TEVIES FAMILY" 30" x 40" Acrylic POR

SHENKER, ILYA

℅ Ligoa Duncan Gallery
22 E. 72nd St. at Madison
New York, N.Y. 10021

2820 W. 8th St., Bldg. 3, Apt. 19-G
Brooklyn, N.Y. 11224

EXHIBITIONS:

Exbtns in Bulgaria, Hungary, Egypt, Italy & USSR

Ligoa Duncan Gallery, N.Y.
Rowe House Gallery, Wash., D.C., one-artist show-1976
Raymond Duncan Galerie, Paris
Nahamkin Gallery, N.Y., 1-artist

COLLECTIONS:

Pushkin Museums in Moscow and Leningrad
Ukrainian Art Museum, Kiev

SHERWOOD, A.

3905 N.W. 37th Place
Gainesville, Florida 32601

GALLERY:
The Gallery
Barnegat Light, N.J. 08006

EXHIBITIONS:
U.S. Embassy,
    Manila, Philippines
Audubon Soc., Wash., D.C.
Va. Museum of Fine Art

AWARDS:
Numerous national, state
    and local awards

COLLECTIONS:
Mobile Art Gallery, Ala.
Lilliputian Fdn, Wash., D.C.
Academy of Fine Art, Md.
Dover Air Force Base
Von Steubon, U.S. Navy
and many others

A. Sherwood is listed in
Who's Who in American Art
and *Who's Who in
International Women.*

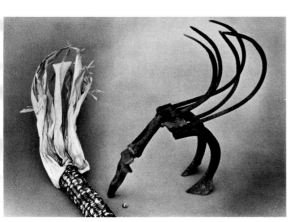

"COCK" 12" Metal $200.

SIGNOR, EUGENIA H.

204 20th Avenue, North
Jacksonville Beach, Fla. 32250

GALLERY:
Beaches Fine Arts Guild
Jax. Bch. Community Ctr.
Jacksonville Beach, Fla.

EXHIBITIONS:
Artist's Cove,
    Atlantic Beach, Fla.
Pablo Plaza, Jax. Bch., Fla.

Flag Pavillion,
    Jacksonville Beach, Fla.
Am. Bicentennial Com'n.,
    Jacksonville, Fla.
First Guar. Bank & Trust,
    Jacksonville, Fla.
Regency Sq., Jacksonville

AWARDS:
Riverside/Avondale Spring
    Art Festival, Merit Award
Beaches Fine Arts Guild,
    Honorable Mention

"BOAT ON INLAND WATERWAY" 9" x 12⅓" $25.

"SEMI-PRECIOUS" 36" x 48" Acrylic $550.

SHIPMAN, HELEN P.

Greenwich, Ct.

GALLERY:
Bell Gallery
202 Fieldpoint Rd.
Greenwich, Ct. 06830

EXHIBITIONS:
Exhibited in galleries &
    in juried shows in Pa.,
    Ct. & N.Y.

COLLECTIONS:
Many private collections

"IN THE BEGINNING (WAS THE WORD)"
22" x 30" Acrylic $300.

SKINNER, ILENE N.
15232 Iron Canyon Rd.
Canyon Country, Ca. 91351

GALLERIES:
Crafty Arts,
  17704 Sierra Hwy.,
  Canyon Cntry, Ca. 91351
Brush Stroke Gallery,
  15232 Iron Canyon Rd.,
  Canyon Cntry, Ca. 91351

EXHIBITIONS:
Laguna Art Festival, Ca.
San Rafael, Ca.; Northridge,
  Ca.; Oakland, Ca.-
  one-artist shows

AWARDS:
Best of Show & many others-
  Watercolors & Oils
Gold Medals for Sculpture,
  Graphics & Etchings

"ISRAELI SOLDIER"
20" x 36" Oil POR

"HOBO'S CAMP" 16" x 20" Oil $350.

SMALL, FAY
212 East Broadway
New York, N.Y. 10002

GALLERIES:
Ligoa Duncan Gallery
  22 E. 72nd St., N.Y.
Galeries Raymond Duncan
  Paris, France

EXHIBITIONS:
Educ. Alliance Galleries
Cayuga Museum of Hist & Art

Salon of 50 States,
  Ligoa Duncan Gallery
Artistes U.S.A.,
  Galeries Raymond Duncan

AWARDS:
Salon of 50 States, Prix
  de Paris, 10 times
Palmes d'Or

COLLECTIONS:
Public & private

SKLAR, ELLEN E.
P.O. Box 309
Marblehead, Mass. 01945

BORN:
Chicago, Sept. 16, 1949

GALLERIES:
Copley Society of Boston
  158 Newbury St.
  Boston, Mass. 01945
Marblehead Arts Assn.
  Marblehead, Mass.
Cape Cod Art Assn.
  Barnstable, Mass.

Rockport Art Assn.
  Rockport, Mass.

EXHIBITIONS:
Copley Soc. of Boston,
  Members Exhibition
Shawmut Bank, Marblehead,
  Mass., 1-artist show
Gloucester Art Walk, Mass.
Marblehead Arts Festival
Cape Cod Artist's Members
  Show
Bangkok, Thailand
Dusitani International Hotel

"COLD MILK, NEW BEDFORD, MASS." 1978 14" x 17"

"END OF THE LINE, BUZZARDS BAY" 1978 14" x 17"

AWARDS:
U.S. Army, Thailand, 1st
  Fashion Design/Watercolor
Westhampton, L.I., N.Y.,
  1st, Ink/Wash
Ariz. Artists, 1st Fashion
  Design, Best of Show

COLLECTIONS:
Shawmut Bank, Mass.
N.H. Savings Bank, Concord

Ellen Sklar studied at the
Quater School of Art; the
University of Arizona;
Traphagen, NYC; Adelphi and
Harvard. She is publicity
director of the Copley Society
and works freelance in Boston.

SMITH, JAY ALFRED
P.O. Box 4244
N. Hollywood, Calif. 91607

BORN:
St. Joseph, Missouri

EXHIBITIONS:
Valley Art Festival,
Sherman Oaks, Calif.

COLLECTIONS:
Numerous private collections
throughout California
and the Midwest

"SALINAS VALLEY, CALIFORNIA" 1978
18" x 24" Oil on Canvas POR

SPRADLEY, WAYNE
911 Hill-Top Road
Pell City, Alabama 35125

GALLERY:
Anne Tutt, 781 College St.
Macon, Georgia 31201

EXHIBITIONS:
Southern Center of Contemp.
Art, Winston-Salem, N.C.
Painters on the Am. Scene,
Charlotte, N.C.
Southern Watercolor Soc.
Alabama Watercolor Soc.

AWARDS:
Over 150 major awards

COLLECTIONS:
Birmingham Museum of Art
Columbus Museum of Art, Ga.
Fine Arts Center of South
Parthenon, Nashville, Tenn.
Many others, public &
private, in U.S. & abroad

"BIG TREES" 30" x 40" Watercolor $1,850.

SMITH, VERN H.
215 Elm Court
Scotch Plains, N.J. 07076

GALLERIES:
Ligoa Duncan Gallery
22 E. 72nd St.
New York, N.Y. 10021
Old Bergen Art Guild
43 W. 33rd St.
Bayonne, N.J.
Ward-Nasse Gallery
178 Prince St.
New York, N.Y.

EXHIBITIONS:
One-artist shows:
Ward-Nasse Gallery, N.Y.
Old Bergen Art Guild,
Regl tour of U.S.
Rutgers Univ., N.J.
Raymond Duncan Gal., Paris
Galleria Bottega dell
Arte, Milan, Italy
Kurasawa Gallery, Tokyo
Salon des Surindependants,
Musee du Luxembourg,
Paris
Academie Intl de Lutece,
Paris

"OF CABBAGES AND THINGS" 24" x 30" Watercolor and Pen & Ink $250.

SOLOMON, SAM
% "The Stan Solomon Collection"
2501 N.W. 5th Avenue
Miami, Florida 33127

BORN:
Ontario, Canada-1913

EXHIBITIONS:
Numerous international exhibitions

COLLECTIONS:
Institutional and private collections
in U.S., Canada, Europe, Mideast
and Far East.

"CONTENTMENT" 48" x 36" Acrylic on Canvas Private Collection NFS

STEELE, STEVEN M.
1727 E. Jamison Ave.
Littleton, Colorado 80122

EXHIBITIONS:
Joe & Emily Lowe Art
  Gallery, Syracuse, N.Y.
Rocky Mountain School of
  Art, Denver, Colorado

COLLECTIONS:
Various private collections
  throughout the U.S.

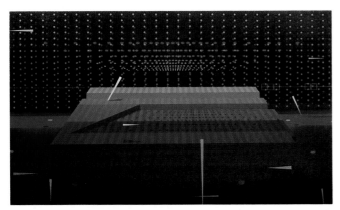

"MONOLITH" 1976 36" x 60" Acrylic POR

STEINBERG, SAUL
% Salerie Maeght
13 rue de Teheran
F-75008, Paris, France

"HEAD" Zinc cut, printed in black,
comp: 14¼" x 18½", sheet: 20⅛" x 26⅛"
Collection, The Museum of Modern Art, New York
Gift of the artist

"BLACK & WHITE #1 - THE CHASE"
22" x 30" Oil & Acrylic $300.

"MEMORIES" 24" x 30" Pastel $500.

STRUEKEN, MARION
50 E. 89th St.
New York, N.Y. 10028

EXHIBITIONS:
11 one-artist & 22 group
  shows throughout the
  U.S., France & Germany

COLLECTIONS:
Numerous private colls. in
  the U.S. & Europe

Marion Strueken studied art
at the National Academy of
Fine Arts as well as at New
School of Social Research in
New York City. Specializing
in portraiture, the artist
is a member of the Pastel
Society of America and the
Art Studio Club.

SWITZER, M.A. BAHL
1111 W. Cook Rd.
Mansfield, Ohio 44906

GALLERY:
Mansfield Art Center
700 Marion Ave.
Mansfield, Ohio 44903

EXHIBITIONS:
Mansfield Fine Arts Guild
Bowling Green State Univ.
Ohio State University
Kent State University

COLLECTIONS:
Ohio State Perman. Coll.

"FEELIN' GOOD" 22" x 30"
Serigraph-Edition of 13 $40.

STOLPIN, WILLIAM R.
12201 Gage Road
Holly, Michigan 48442

GALLERIES:
SuAllen Galleries
3485 Beecher Rd.
Flint, Michigan 48504
Left Bank Gallery
503 East St.
Flint, Michigan 48503

EXHIBITIONS:
41st Flint Annual
Intl. Platform Assn.
Left Bank Gallery

AWARDS:
Intl. Platform Assn., Wash.,
D.C., 1st in Graphics,
Honorable Mention

COLLECTIONS:
Smithsonian Institution,
Natl. Air & Space Museum
Numerous private collections

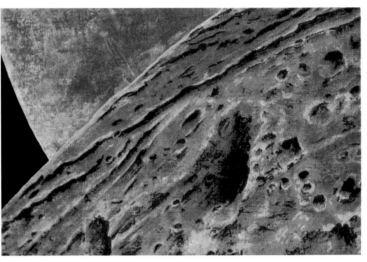

"PHOBOS" 26" x 20" Serigraph-Edition of 25 $35.

"PASSING STORM" 20" x 24" Oil

SUN, LARS ERIK
242 W. 10th St., Apt. 64
New York, N.Y. 10014

EXHIBITIONS:
Greer Gallery
Collector Gallery
Whitney Museum
Brooklyn Museum

AWARDS:
Huntington Hartford
Fellowship

COLLECTIONS:
Museum of Modern Art
Portrait of Sister Kenny
for State of N.Y.
Edward G. Robinson Coll.
Sam Goldwyn, Jr.
Nelson Rockefeller
Vassar College
Arnold Weissen Burger
Margaret Leighton

"BACKYARD" 20" x 25" Oil

SZATHMÁRY, KARA

White Dwarf Studio
Box 295
Dunham, Quebec, Canada JOE 1MO

BORN:
Germany, 1946

EXHIBITIONS:
Art Brome I, Group Show-1976

"THE GAMBLERS" 1975 16" x 20" Acrylic on Gesso NFS

COSMIC SYMBIOSIS

. . . is the continuing web of interrelationships and influences that bind together life on Earth with the moon, the sun, stars, galaxies and other phenomena in an evolving universe.

When modern art is viewed as a periodic table, Cosmic Symbiosis emerges as an isotope of Paul Hartal's element, Lyrical Conceptualism. Basically, the artist attempts to paint in the light that emerges from the boundary between the conscious and the unconscious parts of Man's psyche. It requires serious commitment and the artist's totality.

The resulting paintings are then psychological photographs or calling cards of the artist's soul. No restrictions are placed on the artist's style, medium or concepts. No barriers are built against traditional art. Furthermore, no attempt is made to isolate oneself from past tradition.

What is presented is merely a reaction to post-formalist trends in contemporary art. It is also a signal to the artists of the last quarter of the 20th century that the time is ripe for a fresh and new notion in art.

Lyrical Conceptualism is an attempt to help bring Man in touch with himself. When viewed in this manner, Cosmic Symbiosis is then an attempt to help bring Man in touch with his surroundings.

"LIFE IN THE UNIVERSE" 1978 16" x 14" Acrylic on Gesso POR

"MANNIE SHAW—IDAHO FIDDLER"
24" x 30" Oil NFS

SWAYNE, ZOA L.
P.O. Box 786
Orofino, Idaho 83544

EXHIBITIONS:
Fed. Rocky Mtn. States
University of Idaho
Valley Art Center, Wash.
1-artist shows in Idaho
and Washington

AWARDS:
Valley Art Center,
Best of Show-1976

Idaho White House Conf. on
Aging, 1st Award
Natl Grange Art Contest,
1st Place & Best of Show

COLLECTIONS:
Massee Mem. Libr., Wichita
Univ. of So. Mississippi,
de Grummond Collection
Idaho Historical Museum
Public & private colls.
in U.S. & Saudi Arabia

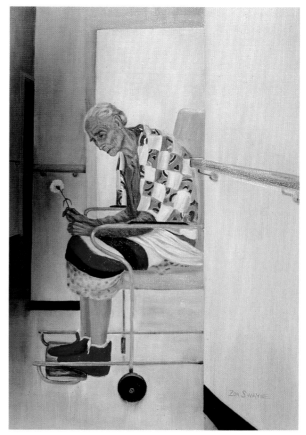

"MOTHER'S DAY" 36" x 48" Oil POR

TAMURA, HERO
10242-4th St., N.W.
Albuquerque, N.M. 87114

"BIOCHEMICAL IMBALANCE" 50" x 34" Acrylic

TAYLOR, WALTER S.
⅛ Bully Hill Vineyards
Greyton H. Taylor Memorial Drive
Hammondsport, N.Y. 14840

Walter S. Taylor is an artist, engraver, woodcarver
and portrait painter.

"MISSION SAN LUIS OBISPO DE TOLOSA" 1978

TEABO, SHARON L.

310 Seventh Ave.
Hinton, W. Va. 25951

EXHIBITIONS:
Rutgers Natl Drawing
    Competition, Camden, N.J.
Intl Women's Year Invit.,
    Capitol Complex, W. Va.
La Grange Natl Competition
    III, Ga.
Communications as Art
    Exbtn., Utrecht, Holland

Intent/77/Drawing Natl.,
    Edinboro, Pa.
Springville Museum, Utah
Herter Gallery, Amherst, Ma.
Sunrise Gallery Graphics
    Annual Drawing Exbt.
and many other intl., natl.
    and regl. shows

COLLECTIONS:
Represented in public &
    private throughout U.S.

"SPRING BREAK" 10" x 19" Linoleum NFS

THIAIS-LOUBRIS

% Ligoa Duncan "Arts"
22 E. 72nd St. at Madison
New York, N.Y. 10021

EXHIBITIONS:
Grand Salons-1979
Several 1-artist shows in
    France-1977 & 78

AWARDS:
Prix de N.Y.-Raymond Duncan

Salon des Artistes Francais
Grand Palais des
    Champs Elysees, Paris
Grand Prix de Rome
Medaille d'Argent, Ville
    de Paris
Medaille de Vermeil, Haute
    Academie de Lutece
Laureate au Salon des
    Palmes Academiques
and many others

"NATURE MORTE AU MELON"
26" x 30" Oil $600.

TARDIF-HÉBERT

15 Romfield Circuit
Thornhill, Ontario
Canada L3H 3H4

Tardif-Hébert is a French-Canadian artist from the
Saguenay Valley, Quebec, Canada. She has had many
exhibitions across Canada and her work is in several
public and private collections.

"5e DIMENSION" 24" x 36" Acrylic POR

TOMASI, ADRIAN

6 Greene Street
New York, N.Y. 10013

BORN:
Providence, R.I., Feb. 12, 1949

GALLERY:
Harkness Gallery, N.Y.C.

COLLECTIONS:
Howard W. Dwyer, V.P.,
   Chrysler International
Hon. Joseph P. Tonelli, Pres.,
   United Paper Workers Intl. Union

Adrian Tomasi received his
education at Providence College
and the School of Visual Arts in
New York City. He has studied with
Robert DeNiro.

"ECSTASY" 30" x 30" Collage

Untitled 30" x 40" Collage

TONG, VERA
23 Chatham Square
New York, N.Y. 10038

BORN:
Hunan, China; Nov. 10, 1938

GALLERY:
United Art Gallery
23 Chatham Square
New York, N.Y. 10038

COLLECTIONS:
Many public & private
collections worldwide

"PORTRAIT OF A FLOWER" 24" x 36" Acrylic $400.

TOMLINSON, RICHARD

319 East 24th Street
New York, N.Y. 10010

EXHIBITIONS:
Harbor Gallery, N.Y.
  News Media, May, 1975
Lowe Art Gallery,
  Contemp. Courtroom Artists,
  Syracuse, N.Y., 1976
Huntsville Museum of Art,
  Traveling Exbtn, 1976-78
Rutgers Univ. Law Library,
  Camden, N.J., Permanent
  Exbtn.
Assoc. of the Bar, City of
  New York, "Courtroom
  Scenes," May 2, 1978

"BROOKLYN SUPREME COURT" 14" x 17" Watercolor Pens
on Strathmore 500 Layout POR

TURNER, JANET E.

567 E. Lassen, Sp. 701
Chico, California 95926

GALLERIES:
Arts & Crafts
  221 W. 2nd, Chico, Ca. 95926

ADI Gallery, San Francisco
Zacha's, Mendocino
Pickard Gallery, Okla. City
Cushing Gallery, Dallas

"RAPTOR RAPTURE" 22½" x 30" Linocut-Serigraph

EXHIBITIONS:
Metro. Museum of Art, N.Y.
Brooklyn Museum
Print Club of Philadelphia
Soc. of Am. Graphic Artists
National Academy of Design
Library of Congress
Boston Printmakers
Bordigliera Biennale, Italy
Kabutoya Gallery, Tokyo
Exhibited in every state &
  42 foreign countries

AWARDS:
Guggenheim Fellowship

Tupperware Art Fdn Fellowship
National Academy of Design,
  Cannon Prize
Numerous purchase awards

COLLECTIONS:
Metro. Museum of Art, N.Y.
Smithsonian, Wash., D.C.
Library of Congress
Victora & Albert, London
Philadelphia Museum of Art
Brooklyn Museum
U.S. Information Service
Biblioteque Natl, Paris
and many others

"BEES IN A TULIP TREE" 16½" x 16½" Etching-Serigraph

"THE MOONLIGHT VISIT" 24" x 30" Oil on Canvas NFS

TOUTZ, CHARLES F.
2440 34th St.
Santa Monica, Calif. 90405

BORN:
Santa Monica, Oct. 22, 1943

COLLECTIONS:
Numerous private collections

Chuck Toutz studied at the Art Center College of Design in Los Angeles and has been engaged in research on his own, looking at life through a new art, "Symbolist Psychological Hyperealism."

The artist on his research:
"The rejection of falseness...What is at stake is the whole human effort to see clearly life, love, hate, violence and death...the Humanist philosophy, to see clearly like a child in prayer! This is the root of my work."

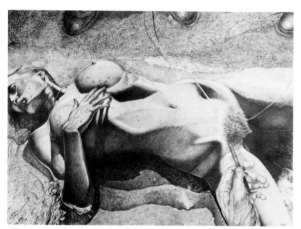

"THROWN AWAY #1" 1978 30" x 40"
Pencil on Cold Pressed Board POR

"HEIDI'S WAIT" 1977 30" x 40"
Pencil on Cold Pressed Board POR

"LIFE OBSCURA #1" 1975-76 24" x 36" Oil on Canvas POR

TOMCHUK, MARJORIE

44 Horton Lane
New Canaan, Connecticut 06840

COLLECTIONS:
Library of Congress, Wash., D.C.
Air & Space Museum, Wash., D.C.
Denver Art Museum, Colorado
DeCordova Museum, Mass.
Nelson Museum, Kansas City, Mo.
Butler Inst. of American Art, Ohio
and numerous others

"VIEW FROM THE FERRY"
18" x 24" 3-color etching
$150. Edition size-120

UNDERWOOD, EVELYN NOTMAN

362 Linden Avenue
East Aurora, N.Y. 14052

BORN:
Canada, Feb. 20, 1898

EXHIBITIONS:
Ligoa Duncan Gallery, N.Y.
Raymond Duncan Gallery,
Paris, France

AWARDS:
Buffalo Society of Artists,
Gold Medal-1977
10 Yellow Steps Gallery,
Purchase Award
East Aurora Art Society
Erie County Fair
and many other top awards

"NEW YORK AT NIGHT" 14" x 20" Watercolor $750.

TWOMBLY, CY

℅ Leo Castelli Gallery
420 W. Broadway
New York, N.Y. 10013

BORN:
Lexington, Va., April 25, 1928

COLLECTIONS:
Represented in public & private
collections in U.S. & abroad

Untitled 1968 68⅛" x 7'3⅛"
Collection, The Museum of Modern Art, New York
Gift of Mr. & Mrs. John R. Jakobson

Emotion is the motivating force behind Lou Utter's art. He paints only what he loves, only what he finds visually exciting. He first searches for the light and dark patterns that give structure to a subject. And he refuses to proceed with a work until he has achieved the indispensable aesthetics of design and proportion. Once the underlying patterns of the picture have been determined, he freely adapts "natural" color to fit the emotional and intuitive needs of the work. The picture is then "completed"—but only to the point at which the imagination of the viewer can participate in the creative process. When a picture looks too finished, he will, as he says, purposely "rough it up."

The freedom of Lou Utter's work is based on a solid technical knowledge of direct and indirect methods, a knowledge acquired in part at the Cincinnati Art Academy and the Gloucester Academy of Fine Arts. He has further enhanced his art background by additional study in the fields of psychology and sociology.

"THE GLOW OF FALL" 24" x 36" Oil $1,600.

"A MOMENT" 12" x 16" Oil $500.

"SHADOWS" 18" x 24" Oil $1,400.

UTTER, LOU
P.O. Box 173
Rockport, Mass. 01966

P.O. Box 177
Easton, Maryland 21601

GALLERIES:
Gloucester Acad. of Fine Arts
  Rockport, Mass. 01966
Addison Gilbert Hosp. Art Gallery
Cape Ann Bank & Trust Art Gallery
Sawyer Free Library Art Gallery

EXHIBITIONS:
Rockport Art Gallery
The Studio Group,
  Pigeon Cove Circle
North Shore Art Gallery
Galeria del Sol
Skidmore College Art Gallery

AWARDS:
Several top awards

COLLECTIONS:
Represented in public & private
  collections

URSO, RICHARD CARL

GALLERY:
The Union Art Gallery
349 Geary Street
San Francisco, Calif. 94102

"SUBMISSION" 1977 3' high Rock Maple

VICTOR, BARRY ALAN

3 Mansion Drive
Hyde Park, N.Y. 12538

EXHIBITIONS:
Numerous exhibitions

COLLECTIONS:
Numerous private throughout
the U.S. & Europe

Barry Alan Victor works in
pastel, marble, wood,
limestone, sheet lead, pen
and ink, oil and charcoal.
His style is realism,
semi-abstract.

"ENTANGLEMENT" 9" x 9½" Pen & Ink $375.

VARES, KEN

208 Goodwin St.
Hayward, California 94544

GALLERIES:
Artists Co-op
1750 Union St., S.F., Ca.
Galerie de Blanche
4th & Townsend, S.F., Ca.
Studio Bronze
208 Goodwin, Hayward, Ca.

EXHIBITIONS:
16 one-artist shows & numerous
group shows

COLLECTIONS:
Triton Museum
Cowboy Hall of Fame/West

Ken Vares is listed in *Who's
Who in the West 1977-78* and
Personalities in the West 1979.

"DUELO CRIOLLO" Cast Aluminum 12" x 20" Unique Casting POR

"NIGHT OF THE SPOUSE HUNTER"
Bronze 12" h. Unique Casting POR

VON SZITANYI-WALEWSKA
631 W. 185th St.
New York, N.Y. 10033

GALLERIES:
Bernheim-Jeune
    83 rue de Fobourg
    St. Honore, Paris, France
La Palette Blue Gal., Paris
Galeria Tritone, Rome
Gal. Duomo, Bari, Italy

EXHIBITIONS:
One-artist shows throughout
    Europe, U.S. & Canada

COLLECTIONS:
Museo Vaticano, Rome
Private collections through-
    out Europe, U.S. & Canada

"THE TREES" 22" x 29" Oil POR

"HAWAIIAN WHALER"
Acrylic on Canvas

WALL, PAT
℅ Tree House Gallery
P.O. Box 310
Langley, Oklahoma 74350

EXHIBITIONS:
Many group & 1-artist incl:
    El Reno Annual
    Tulsa Sailcraft

AWARDS:
Philbrook Annual, 1st Place
Carnagie Exbtn, Detroit

Grove Annual, 1st Prize &
    Best of Show
and others

COLLECTIONS:
Will Rogers Memorial
Bacone College, Muskogee
Public & private throughout
    U.S., Canada & Japan

COMMISSIONS:
Special comm., "Emma West,"
    great granddaughter of
    Red Cloud, Chief of
    Oglala Sioux

WARD, BETHEA
9614 Val Verde
Houston, Texas 77063

"OLD DALLAS COURTHOUSE"
14½" x 21½" Watercolor POR

EXHIBITIONS:
One-artist shows:
    Star of Republ Musm, Tx
    Houston Publ Library, Tx
    1st Natl Bank, San Anton.
Juried shows:
    Wichita Cent Natl, Kan.
    Witte Musm & Coppini, SA
    Panhandle Plains Musm
    McNamara-O'Connor Musm
    and many others

AWARDS:
TFAA-Laguna Gloria Museum,
    1st Place-Watercolor
San Antonio Art League,
    Wofford Purchase Prize
    and many others

COLLECTIONS:
Public & private

WASHINGTON, JENNI S.
11439 S. Racine St.
Chicago, Illinois 60643

GALLERY:
Dusable Museum
740 E. 56th
Chicago, Ill. 60637

EXHIBITIONS:
American Academy of Art
South Side Art Center
Univ. of Chicago,
    Center for Contin. Educ.

"PAPA BABYSITTING" 8" x 9¼" Watercolor $100.

WARHOL, ANDY
  Andy Warhol Enterprises
  860 Broadway
  New York, N.Y. 10003

BORN:
  Cleveland, Ohio, Aug. 8, 1931

GALLERY:
  Leo Castelli Gallery
  4 E. 77th St.
  New York, N.Y. 10021

EXHIBITIONS:
  Many group & one-artist shows

AWARDS:
  Los Angeles Film Festival

"SIDNEY JANIS" 1967 Photosensitive gelatin and tinted lacquer
on silkscreen on wood frame, 7'11⅛" x 6'4⅛"
Collection, The Museum of Modern Art, New York
The Sidney & Harriet Janis Collection, Gift to the
Museum of Modern Art, New York

GALLERIES:
  El Gatito Gallery
    Los Gatos, Calif.
  S.F. Artists Co-op. Gallery
    San Francisco, Calif.

EXHIBITIONS:
  Triton Museum of Art, Santa
    Clara, Ca., 1-artist show
  Other 1-artist & group shows

AWARDS:
  Over 40, including 6 in 1978

COLLECTIONS:
  Triton Museum
  Monterey Peninsula Museum
  Private collections in U.S.,
    Japan & U.S.S.R.

WATERMAN, LORI
562 Gerona Road
Stanford, California 94305

"WOMAN OF MEXICO" 12" x 15"
Woodcut Print $125.

"SUMMER BREEZE" 22" x 28" Oil $800.

WATKINS, CURTIS W.
519 S. Michigan
Howell, Michigan 48843

EXHIBITIONS:
  The Artist Guild of Detroit,
    One-artist show
  Platt Gallery, Ann Arbor
  Golden Gallery, Brighton,
    Mich., One-artist show
  Grand Rapids Art Museum
    Mich. Painters & Printmakers
  and many other natl & regl shows

Curtis Watkins' paintings are executed while the artist is in a somnambule level of hypnosis. This level of hypnosis is similar to sleepwalking, where the person has no recollection when he awakens. The artist considers this as research into the study of the visualization process of the subconscious mind.

Watkins studied art at Kendall School of Design in Grand Rapids and the Ann Arbor Art Center. He is a member of the Association to Advance Ethical Hypnosis and gives lecture/demonstrations on his research.

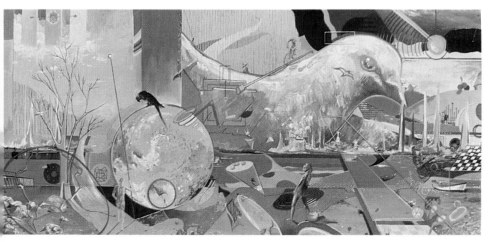

AWARDS:
  Best of Show & numerous other
    awards of excellence

COLLECTIONS:
  Kraus Hypnosis Center, Detroit

'REVERIE" 1976 15" x 30" Oil NFS

WEIL, MEG

240 Central Park South
New York, N.Y. 10019

Studio: 10 E. 23rd St.
New York, N.Y. 10010

EXHIBITIONS:
One-artist shows:
 Galerie Creuse, Paris
 Galerie Boler, Paris

Am Soc. Contemporary Artists
Artists Equity Assoc., N.Y.
N.Y. Soc. Women Artists
National Arts Club
Am. Artists in Paris
Salon de l'Art Libre, Paris
and others in U.S. & abroad

"NEO TOTEM" 15" x 10" x ³/₁₆ Slate POR
17¾" high with base

"CONTINUITY" 9¼" x 12" x 4" Limestone POR
12" high with base

AWARDS:
Arts Sciences Lettres,
 Bronze Medal, France
Am. Soc. Contemporary Artists

COLLECTIONS:
Collections in N.Y.,
 France & Israel

WHITING, PEGGY L.

9805 Pamela Drive
Temperance, Michigan 48182

EXHIBITIONS:
Toledo Fed. Shows, 1974–78
Detroit Scarab Club, Gold &
 Silver Medal Shows
Participated in 2-artist show,
 "Expressions," Detroit

AWARDS:
Molly Morpeth Canaday Award,
 Outstanding Painting, 1978
Scarab Club Gold Medal Show,
 Detroit, 2nd Place
Scarab Club Silver Medal
 Show, Detroit, 2nd Place

COLLECTIONS:
Represented in public &
 private in several states

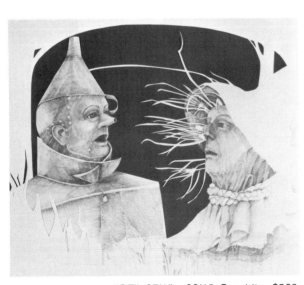

"OZ" 27½" x 30½" Graphite $300.

"COLOR TV" 27" x 22" Graphite $300.

WENNET, ELLIOTT
℅ The Stan Solomon Collection
2501 N.W. 5th Avenue
Miami, Florida 33127

BORN:
Queens, N.Y., 1945

EXHIBITIONS:
Numerous international exhibitions

AWARDS:
Many international awards

COLLECTIONS:
Commercial and private collections
in the U.S., Canada, Paris,
London, Hong Kong, Japan and Israel

"MOUNTAIN VIEW" 36" x 40" Acrylic on Canvas Private Collection NFS

"STANDING NUDE BACK VIEW-OPUS 2" 34" x 28" Pastel POR

WILLIAMS, EVELYN SINGER
479 Walton Ferry Road
Hendersonville, Tennessee 37075

GALLERIES:
Lynn Kottler Gallery
3 East 65th St.
New York, N.Y. 10021
Gallery III
122 Stadium Dr.
Hendersonville, Tenn. 37075
Blue Door Gallery
Old Kit Carson Rd.
Taos, New Mexico 87571

EXHIBITIONS:
Gallery III, Hendersonville, Revolving show
Lynn Kottler, N.Y., Feb., 1978
Bittner's, Louisville, Ky., Group show
Fairfield Glades, Cookeville, Tenn.,
2-artist show with Xavier Ironsides
One-artist shows:
New Public Library, Chickasha, Okla.
Discoveries, Inc., Okla. City, Okla.
Art Center, Ft. Smith, Ark.
The Parthenon, Nashville, Tenn.
Technological Inst., Cookeville, Tenn.
Gallery III, Hendersonville, Tenn.
Cumberland County Playhouse, Tenn.
Fields Gallery, Tulsa, Okla.

COLLECTIONS:
Cumberland County Playhouse
Paul Crabtree
Mr. & Mrs. Myron Kinley
Numerous private collections

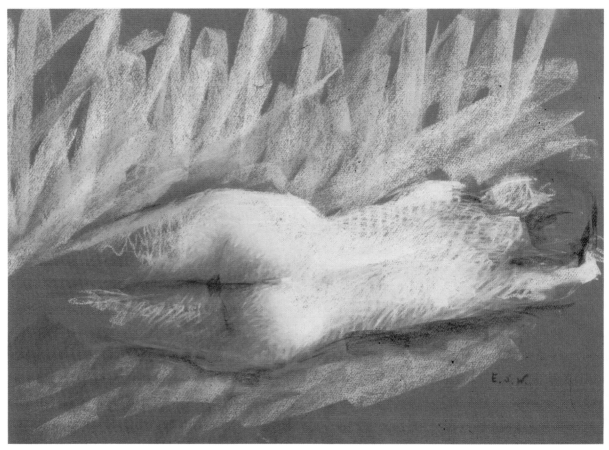

"RECLINING NUDE-OPUS 3" 24" x 28" Pastel POR

"SEATED NUDE-OPUS 1" 34" x 28" Oil POR

WILLIAMS, EVELYN SINGER

"ROSA" 33" x 31" Fast Pastel, Casein Underpainting POR

"THE 5 LIVES OF PROFESSOR PHOGBOUND" Composition art

WINDELL, VIOLET BRUNER

R.R. 1, Box 108
Ramsey, Indiana 47166

GALLERY:
The Cabbage Patch
Leavenworth, Indiana 47137

EXHIBITIONS:
Lincoln Hills Annual Show,
Cannelton, Indiana
Squire Boone Caverns,
Mauckport, Indiana

AWARDS:
Harrison County Fair, Indiana,
1st Place

COLLECTIONS:
Indiana State Library, Indianapolis
Indiana University, Bloomington
Public Library, Louisville, Ky.
Public Library, Corydon, Indiana
Pendle Hill Library, Wallingford, Pa.

Born in DePauw, Indiana on November 1, 1922,
Violet Bruner Windell is listed in the current
edition of *Who's Who in the Midwest.*

An artist of both the brush and pen, Ms. Windell
is also an author. To date, she has penned
three books, "The Fairy Bells Tinkle Afar,"
"Rainbows and Daisies" and "Which Man Named
Sunderland," all biographical writings. The
artist says of these works:
  "It was important to me to get the third
  section of the biography into print
  because *Which Man* takes the reader into
  the nittygritty of adult human behavior.
  What tensions are going to arise in the
  protagonist of the story, the art student,
  if she marries the young man nearer her
  age while having so much background or
  parallel situations and dialog for comparison
  with the older, more sophisticated (so he
  thinks!) brother? *The Fairy Bells* was a
  study in the early preferences and practices
  that predict later choices in the arts.
  Rainbows focuses on teacher influences on
  student thought. In *Which Man* we can still
  ask the question of beginning adulthood, how
  does the sleeping with another person, how
  does the carrying of another person within
  or beside one's body affect that stream-of-
  consciousness thought?"

In an article in "The Paper," Corydon, Indiana,
the writer notes:
  "Violet Bruner Windell is indeed a unique woman.
  No one else with the talents of writer and
  artist has been able to reconcile publicly
  their feelings about their private lives and
  their wordly contributions, as Violet. While
  there are many who will not agree that she
  should open her ideas for all to see, there
  are those who will recognize themselves in this
  woman and wish secretly that they too could say,
  'The children are raised. It's a whole new ball
  game now. I'm finally doing all the things
  I've wanted to do.'"

Woodcutting

WYETH, JAMES
Chadds Ford, Pa. 19317

BORN:
Wilmington, Del., July 6, 1946

COLLECTIONS:
William Farnsworth Museum,
 Rockland, Maine
Brandywine River Museum,
 Chadds Ford, Pa.
Delaware Art Museum

Jamie Wyeth works in oils and watercolors and is a member of the National Academy of Design, the American Watercolor Society and the National Endowment for the Arts.

"ANDY WARHOL" 1976 Gouache, Watercolor, Pencil, Sheet: 16⅛″ x 13⅜″
Collection, The Museum of Modern Art, New York
Acquired with matching funds from Mrs. Walter N. Thayer and the
National Endowment for the Arts.

WILL, S.
P.O. Box 8457
Van Nuys, California 91409

EXHIBITIONS:
Numerous in L.A., Calif.

AWARDS:
Various first awards

COLLECTIONS:
Many private collections
throughout the U.S.,
Mexico, Germany & France

"MOUNT OLYMPUS" 24" x 36" Oil on Canvas $2,000
©1978 S. Will

WILNER, MARIE
% Ligoa Duncan "Arts"
22 E. 72nd St. at Madison
New York, N.Y. 10021

After painting for a number of years and participating in hundreds of exhibitions, gaining awards and recognitions, Marie Wilner is turning towards sculpture. Inspired by Isadore Duncan, she is creating dancing figures in clay to be turned into bronze.

"ISADORE DUNCAN" Bronze or Hydrocal Casts POR

"VASE"
8" x 22" Clay
NFS

"TEA POT"
5" x 7" POR

WOOLFSON, JEAN
2477 Becket Drive
Union City, California 94587

Jean Woolfson creates pottery and custom made dinnerware in both classic and sculptural forms. She performs one-artist shows for galleries and charitable organizations.

ZARFOS, GLENN M.
404 Commerce Street
New Cumberland, W. Va. 26047

Glenn Zarfos has appeared in many one-artist shows and has received numerous awards.

GALLERIES:
Famous French Galleries
16 West Main Street
Westminister, Md. 21157
Bogarad Gallery of Fine Ar
326 Penco Road
Weirton, W. Va. 26062

"MR. SHOES"
27½" x 17½"
$400.

ARTISTS'
DIRECTORY
AND
INDEX

★Directory listing only

CRAWFORD, RUTH A.
304 Rio Vista Pl.
Santa Fe, N.M. 87501 46

CULLNAN, SHARON M.
Rt. 5, 127th St.
Lemont, Il. 60439 48

CURTIS, LOIS
Box 854
Grants, N.M. 87020 48

DABBS, MIRIAM
℅ Ligoa Duncan Gallery
22 E. 72nd St.
New York, N.Y. 10021 48

DAIGLE, ROGER R.
2423 W. Morton
Denison, Tx. 75020 48

DALI, SALVADOR
Hotel St. Regis
New York, N.Y. 10022 49

DANILA
P.O. Box 503
Southern Pines, N.C. 28387 49

Da PRATO, JOHN
61 Puffer La.
Sudbury, Ma. 01776 50

DAVIS, OLIVE L.
Box 598, 415 S. 5th
Basin, Wy. 82410 . . . . *

DAVIS-BANKS, PHYLLIS EILEEN
5714 College Dr.
Anchorage, Ak. 99504 49

DeBAUN, BARRY
Trail Motel, Rt. 28
Boiceville, N.Y. 12412 50

De CRESCENZO, DOMINIC
℅ Ligoa Duncan Gallery
22 E. 72nd St.
New York, N.Y. 10021 51

de KOONING, WILLEM
Woodbine Dr.
The Springs
East Hampton, N.Y. 11973 52

de NASSAU, JOANNA
35 Old Church Rd.
Greenwich, Ct. 06830 . . . . *

DENNIS, LUCILLE
710 S. 8th St.
Terre Haute, In. 47807 . . . . *

DeVITO, TERESA M.
417 Newton St.
Fairmont, WV 26554 52

DINE, JIM
℅ The Pace Gallery
32 E. 57th St.
New York, N.Y. 53

DOEBRICH, LEE G.
℅ Mary Joyce
622 Hope St.
Providence, R.I. 02906 52

DORRIS, PARKY
Rt. 4
Cleveland, Ga. 30528 52

DUNCAN, LIGOA
℅ Ligoa Duncan "Arts"
22 E. 72nd St.
New York, N.Y. 10021 54

EBBERT, GEORGE C.
616 N. Rush St.
Chicago, Il. 60611 55

EGAN, JACQUES L.
809 N. Broad St.
Adrian, Mi. 49221 57

ELIASON, BIRDELL
12 N. Owen St.
Mt. Prospect, Il. 60056 56

ERKERD, WILLIE J.
39 Arch St.
New Haven, Ct. 06519 . . . . *

FAY, KEITH L.
Box 1116
Jackson Hole, Wy. 83001 57

FELTON, LORI K.
1401 Allston
Houston, Tx. 77008 57

FERRIE, THOMAS J.
93 Pineland Ave.
Worcester, Ma. 58

FILIPPONE, BASIL
74 Christine Dr.
E. Hanover, N.J. 07936 58

FINSON, HILDRED A.
304 S. Wilson
Jefferson, Ia. 50129 59

FOLLETT, MARY V.
1440 Park Ave.
River Forest, Il. 60305 59

FOOTE, J. LANELL
137 S. 2nd, East
Brigham City, Ut. 84302 59

FRANKENTHALER, HELEN
173 E. 94th St.
New York, N.Y. 10028 60

FREDERIKSEN, ARNI
70 Willow St.
Brooklyn Hgts., N.Y. 11201 59

FREEMAN, FRED L.
2949 Lilac Rd.
Beloit, Wi. 53511 61

GALE, WILLIAM
1812 Bruce Ave.
Roseville, Mn. 55113 . . . . *

GARDINER, PAULINE S.
P.O. Box 473
Seabrook, Tx. 77586 61

GATES, SHARON LEE
7003 E. Cheney Dr.
Scottsdale, Az. 85253 . . . . 62, 63, 64, 65

GAZONAS, ALEXANDER G.
2 Commodore Rd.
Worcester, Ma. 01602 61

GELLER, BUNNY
13 Oakdale Dr.
Westbury, N.Y. 11590 . . . . 66, 67, 68, 69

GENTILE, JOHN O.
114 Corbett Rd.
Stoughton, Ma. 02072 61

GERARD, BARBARA
1623 Third Ave.
New York, N.Y. 10028 72

GHAMDI, MOHAMMED S.
284 12th Ave., #1
San Francisco, Ca. 94118 . . . . 70, 71

GIFFUNI, FLORA B.
180-16 Dalny Rd.
Jamaica, N.Y. 11432 72

GINSBURG, DAVID WILLIAM
4539 Luxemburg Ct., #201
Lake Worth, Fl. 33463 . . . . *

GOMER, GARY
Park Towne Pl. No.
Philadelphia, Pa. 19130 72

**GONZALEZ, RICHARD DANIEL
("RICARDO")**
967 D. St.
Hayward, Ca. 94541 73

GOSNEY, N. RUTH
271 S. 6th St.
Middleport, Ohio 45760 75

**GRAZIANO, MERCOLINO
FLORENCE**
1413 Highland Ave.
Plainfield, N.J. 07060 73

GREEN, VINCE
31961 Trevor Ave.
Hayward, Ca. 94544 74

GREGORIO, FRANK
7547 W. Monroe St.
Niles, Il. 60648 76

GREGORIO, PETER A.
304 E. Davis Blvd.
Tampa, Fl. 33606 77

GRILLO, DONATO
915 Green Hills Dr.
Ann Arbor, Mi. 48105 . . . . *

GROTEY, GARY
℅ Artco, Inc.
Rt. 2-Box 109 Cuba Rd.
Long Grove, Il. 60047 78

GUIDOTTI, JOHANNES S.
3600 Dawson
Warren, Mi. 48092 78

GUILLOUX, CHRISTINE
℅ Ligoa Duncan "Arts"
22 E. 72nd St.
New York, N.Y. 10021 78

GUNKEL, VIRGINIA P.
201 Freda Dr.
Pacheco, Ca. 94553 79

HAFFORD, JEANNETTE C.
658 Columbia Ave.
Palmerton, Pa. 18071 79

HAMANN, CAROL
℅ Atlantic Gallery
81 Atlantic Ave.
Brooklyn, N.Y. 11201 79

**HAMBLET, MARGARET
WOOLDRIDGE**
514 Lore Ave.
Wilmington, De. 19809 80

HARRIS, MURIEL B.
301 Plainfield Rd.
Edison, N.J. 08817 80

HARRISON, PHILIP
2714 Penn Towers
Philadelphia, Pa. 19103 81

HARTAL, PAUL
P.O. Box 1012
St. Laurent, Montreal
Quebec, H4L 4W3 Canada 81

HATFIELD, DAVID
240 W. 38th St.
New York, N.Y. 10018 82

HATHAWAY, HYLDA KOHL
5829 S. Datura, Apt. 517
Littleton, Co. 80120 . . . . *

HAVRILLA, JOHN R.
88 E. Maple St.
Trescow, Pa. 18254 80

HAY, GEORGE AUSTIN
Hay Ave.
Johnstown, Pa. 83

*Directory listing only

HAYNES, KATHERINE H.
Star Rt. 3, Box 154
Bonners Ferry, Id. 83805 82

HODGES, S.
830 E. 14th
Ada, Ok. 74820 84

HOEFLINGER, WILLIAM P.
33 Headley Ave.
Morris Plains, N.J. 07950 . . . . *

HOFFMAN, HARRY Z.
3910 Clark's La.
Baltimore, Md. 21215 84

HOUCK, PEGI
4th Ave.
Hastings, Pa. 16646 84

HUDSON, JULIE H.
4224 Beverly Dr.
Dallas, Tx. 75205 84

IMANA, JORGE G.
2168 Chatsworth Blvd.
San Diego, Ca. 92107 85

INDIANA, ROBERT
2 Spring St.
New York, N.Y. 10012 85

ISOM, JOHN E.
124 W. Scott Ave.
Forrest City, Ar. 72335 85

ITTNER, SCOTT
4067 Magnolia Pl.
St. Louis, Mo. 63110 . . . . *

JACKSON, HERBERT DAN
London La., Rt 3
Ringgold, Ga. 30736 86

JAFFE, SYLVIA A.
11 Burning Tree La.
Boca Raton, Fl. 33432 . . . . *

JANELLE, RHEAUME
R.R. #2, Box 158
Danville, PQ, Canada J0A 1A0 86

JARDINE, ELLEN A.
15 Hamilton Dr.
Madison, Ct. 06443 86

JENKINS, PAUL
31 E. 72nd St.
New York, N.Y. 10021 87

JERMYN, ROBERT J.
3586 Powder Mill Rd.
Beltsville, MD. 20705 88

JESSEN, SHIRLEY A.
90 Fifth St.
Garden City, N.Y. 11530 89

JOHNS, JASPER
225 E. Houston St.
New York, N.Y. 10002 88

JOHNSON, D. KENDRICK
P.O. Box 7162
Carmel, Ca. 93921 88

JOHNSON, EMILY L.
1072 W. Hollis St.
Nashua, N.H. 03060 . . . . *

JOHNSON, GWENAVERE A.
Tree Tops Studio
2054 Booksin Ave.
San Jose, Ca. 95125 90

JOHNSON, JANICE E.
Rt. 1, Box 23
Erwin, N.C. 28339 90

JOHNSON, MYRNA J.
1201 S. Court House Rd., Apt. 610
Arlington, Va. 22204 91

JONES, ERNEST LEE
1015 Elkin St.
Norfolk, Va. 23523 92

KAMADA, ITOHEI
% Ligoa Duncan "Arts"
22 E. 72nd St.
New York, N.Y. 10021 93

KAPRAL, PEGGY
Rt. 2, Box 370
Eatonville, Wa. 98328 94

KAROL, REUBEN H.
261 S. Adelaide Ave.
Highland Park, N.J. 08904 92

KARR, CHARLEE MARIE
4901 Garfield
Groves, Tx. 77619 92

KEISTER, ROY
15800 Highland Dr.
San Jose, Ca. 95127 95

KENT, LESTER GRANT
22315 Western Blvd.
Hayward, Ca. 94541 96

KEPP, CAROL S
810 Ivanhoe Dr.
Port St. Lucie, Fl. 33452 98

KNAPP, VIRGINIA
Ring Neck Rd.
Drawer H
Remsenburg, N.Y. 11960 98

KNIGHT, JAY
36 Hanrahan Ave.
Farmingville, L.I., N.Y. 11738 97

KNUTSON, DONALD L.
120 S. Martin
Visalia, Ca. 93277 100

KOCHMAN, ALEXANDRA
5453 N. Virginia Ave.
Chicago, Il. 60625 . . . . *

KOLAWOLE, LAWRENCE COMPTON
357-B Scott St.
San Francisco, Ca. 94117 99

KUNARD, ROBBIE C.
677 42nd Ave.
San Francisco, Ca. 94121 98

LAMBERT, OLGA
770 Ocean Ave., Apt. E3
Brooklyn, N.Y. 11226 . . . . *

LaMONTAGNE, ARMAND
% Beverland Enterprises, Inc.
P.O. Box 250, Dept. AR 100
Oldsmar, Fl. 33557 . . . . 102, 103

LAND, M. SCHWABEN
1375 Oak Ave.
Los Altos, Ca. 94022 100

LANGSTON, JUDY A.
1122 Kemman Ave.
La Grange Park, Il. 60525 100

LARSEN, BEN
832 Camino Ranchitos
Santa Fe, N.M. 87501 101

LAUTTENBACH, CAROL
39 Ridgewood Rd.
Wallingford, Ct. 06492 104

LEHRER, JACK C.
250 Park Ave., So.
New York, N.Y. 10003 104

LEIGHNINGER, PEGGY
1124 Midway Rd.
Northbrook, Il. 60062 105

LEIPZIG, MEL
38 Abernethy Dr.
Trenton, N.J. 08618 104

LENNOX, SHIRLEY A.
Lennox Art Studio
P.O. Box 405
Morton, N.Y. 14508 106

LIBERMAN, ALEXANDER
173 E. 70th St.
New York, N.Y. 10021 104

LICHTENSTEIN, ROY
P.O. Box 1369
Southampton, N.Y. 11968 106

LIEBERMAN, JEFFREY H.
405 Hendrix St.
Philadelphia, Pa. 19116 107

LIM, KAC-KEONG K.K.
1004 Baylor Dr.
Binghamton, N.Y. 13903 107

LOEB, JANET
3634 Seventh Ave., Apt. 14G
San Diego, Ca. 92103 . . . . *

LONG, MAE J.
4071 Schiller Pl.
St. Louis, Mo. 63116 108

LUNDIN, MARY M.
Box 2852
W. Palm Beach, Fl. 33402 108

LUNDQUIST, DOROTHY (DEA)
P.O. Box 354
Kenwood, Ca. 95452 109

LUTZOW, JACK A.
240 Dolores
San Francisco, Ca. 94103 110

LYNES, WILLIAM F.
3380 Forrest Hill Rd.
Powder Springs, Ga. 30073
    GALLERY & STUDIO:
    The Lynes Den
    3380 Forrest Hill Rd.
    Powder Springs, Ga. 30073 . . . . *

MACIEL, JIM
2 John St.
New York, N.Y. 10038 110

MALINAS, NICOLAS
% Ligoa Duncan "Arts"
22 E. 72nd St.
New York, N.Y. 10021 110

MANCHESKI, MARCIA
2010 S. Williams St.
Denver, Co. 80210 110

MARABLE, SIMEON-DAVID de PAUL
18 Spindle Tree Rd.
Levittown, Pa. 19056 111

MARTINELLI, SHERI
P.O. Box 1044
Pacifica, Ca. 94044 111

MARTINEZ, LOUIS M., Jr.
1357 W. 76th St.
Hialeah, Fl. 33014 111

MARTINEZ, YOLANDA
61 Walker Ave.
Closter, N.J. 07624 112

MARTMER, WILLIAM P.
4356 Bundy Rd.
Coloma, Mi. 49038 112

MARZEC, WANDA
62-B Glenwood Ave.
Elmwood Park, N.J. 07407 113

MASSEY, WILLIAM W., Jr.
3420-Z University Blvd., S.
Jacksonville, Fl. 32216 118

*Directory listing only

MAURER, LYDIA V.
Box 403/4th & Silver
Lake City, Co. 81235 112

MAX, PETER
Peter Max Enterprises
118 Riverside Dr.
New York, N.Y. 10024 113

McCALLA, MARY E.
264 Scenic Ridge Rd.
Kalispell, Mt. 59901 113

McGEHEE, PAUL
4055 N. 35th St.
Arlington, Va. 22207 . . . . 114, 115, 116, 117

McKENZIE, E.M.
4735 21st St., N., Apt. A-6
Arlington, Va. 22207 118

McMAHON, SARAN
Rt. 2, Box 217
Alta Loma, Tx. 77510 118

McVEIGH, MIRIAM T.
8200 14th St., North
St. Petersburg, Fl. 33702 119

McVICAR, JANICE
26180 Parkside Dr.
Hayward, Ca. 94542 120

MEIXNER, MARY L.
1007 Lincoln Way, Apt. 4
Ames, Ia. 50010 120

MERRILL, PAT
511 Woodlawn St.
Venice, Ca. 90291 . . . . *

MILLER, DOROTHY DAWE
4721 Rodman St., N.W.
Washington, D.C. 20016 121

MILLER, DOROTHY R.
1413 Cypress Ave.
Elsmere Pk. Apts. #3
Wilmington, De. 19805 . . . . *

MILLS, JOYCE L.
P.O. Box 142
Newton Jct., N.H. 03859 . . . . *

MITCHELL, DOROTHY S.
114 Dewhurst Dr., #23A
San Antonio, Tx. 78213 120

MOCK-MORGAN, MAVERA E.
#3 Carvel Circle
Washington, D.C. 20016 121

MOORE, HENRY
% Marlborough Gallery
39 Old Bond St.
London, England 122

MORALES, ALBERT
100 Lincoln Ave.
Mineola, N.Y. 11501 121

MORFORD, JOHN A.
P.O. Box 261
Rexburg, Id. 83440 122

MORTIMER, CAROLYN G.
Commissioner's Pike
Elmer, N.J. 08318 122

MOTHERWELL, ROBERT
909 North St.
Greenwich, Ct. 06830 123

MOULTRIE, JAMES
131 Governors Rd.
Lakewood, N.J. 08701 123

MURPHY, MARIE L.
4949 Battery La.
Bethesda, Md. 20014 124

MUSGRAVE, REAL
3611 Marsh La. Pl.
Dallas, Tx. 75220 123

MUSIAL, ANDREW
41-B Linwood Ave.
Elmwood Park, N.J. 07407 125

NADALINI, LOUIS E.
154 Lynn St.
Seattle, Wa. 98109 126

NAKACHE, MARGARET
1448 Woodacre Dr.
McLean, Va. 22101 125

NAOMI, JILL
405 Hendrix St.
Philadelphia, Pa. 19116 125

NARDONE, VINCENT J.
75 Essex Ave.
Maplewood, N.J. 07040 127

NARIKAWA, SHIGERU S.N.
6 Jones St., #4B
New York, N.Y. 10014 128

NASRI, GERTRUD
1230 S.E. Morrison, #403
Portland, Or. 97214 130

NEBEL, KARL
166-25 Powells Cove Blvd., Apt. 20 L
Beechhurst, N.Y. 11357 129

NEVELSON, LOUISE
29 Spring St.
New York, N.Y. 10012 130

OILAR, JOHN R.
813 S. 10th St.
Lafayette, In. 47905 131

OLDENBURG, CLAES
% Petersburg Press
18 E. 81st St.
New York, N.Y. 10028 130

OWENS, SHERMAN T., II
519 Mar Vista Ave., Apt. 4
Pasadena, Ca. 91106 . . . . *

PANGALOS, MARIA
159-00 Riverside Dr., W.
New York, N.Y. 10032 131

PARDO, LYNN
12065 Edgewater Dr.
Lakewood, Ohio 44107 131

PARTIDA, ELENA
3691 N.E. 15th Ave.
Pompano Beach, Fl. 33064 131

PEER, PAULA E.
Box 502
Blue Hill, Me. 04614 134

PIPER, MAL
1823 Woodside Dr.
Arlington, Tx. 76013 132

POHOLE, FRANK A.
753 39th St.
Brooklyn, N.Y. 11232 133

POLLEY, EDGAR L.
1806 Beachwood Ave.
New Albany, In. 47150 134

POPPE, JANUS
31 San Miguel Dr.
Chula Vista, Ca. 92011 . . . . *

PRAZEN, GARY F.
Box 146N, Rt. 1
Helper, Ut. 84526 135

PRENTISS, TINA
Wilmington, Ma. 01887 134

PURDY, ROBERT CLEAVER
851 Lexington Ave.
New York, N.Y. 10021 134

RANDALL, PAULA
441 Ramona Ave.
Sierra Madre, Ca. 91024 137

RANDLETT, STUART E.
Box 483, Menwith Hill Sta.
APO N.Y. 09210 136

RAUSCHENBERG, ROBERT
381 Lafayette St.
New York, N.Y. 10003 138

RAVOIRA, JAMES
138 Bull St.
Charleston, S.C. 29401 137

REEVES, BETTY-JOY
24 Gramercy Park
New York, N.Y. 10003 139

REINEL, ROLAND
"The Citadel"
P.O. Box 325
Stuart, Fl. 33494 137

RINALDO, KAREN A.
29 Great Bay Rd.
Teaticket, Ma. 02536 140

RIVERS, LARRY
92 Little Plains Rd.
Southampton, N.Y. 11968 141

RIZZO
% Joy Rubin Art Gallery
101 Hollywood Fashion Center
Hollywood, Fl. 33023 139

ROSENBERG, YETTA
16605 Aldersyde Dr.
Shaker Hts., Oh. 44120 142

ROSS, JO
Rt. #11, Box 220
Greenville, S.C. 29611 . . . . *

RUCKER, JILL
246 Vassar Ave.
Newark, N.J. 07112 . . . . *

SALLÈ, JACQUES
365 Seventh Ave.
New York, N.Y. 10001 142

SAULE, VIGEO
425 Riverside Dr.
New York, N.Y. 10025 142

SCHAUER, WALBURGA "WALLY"
218 Avenida Rosa #1
San Clemente, Ca. 92672 143

SCHEFFLER, FRAN
4344A Seagrape Dr.
Lauderdale-By-The-Sea, Fl. 33308 143

SCHIMPF, RUTH 'ENGLISH'
2154 W. Spring St.
Lima, Oh. 45805 143

SEBELIST, MARGO
107 Trout Valley Dr.
Hendersonville, Tn. 37075 . . . . *

**SEYMOUR, FLORENCE
(Mrs. Russell)**
3684 Hedrick St.
Jacksonville, Fl. 32205 . . . . *

SHAFFETT, RICHARD, Jr.
956 Pomelo Ave.
Sarasota, Fl. 33579 143

SHAPIRO, DAVID S.
RD 1, Box 51A Hall Rd.
Friendsville, Pa. 18818 144

SHEA, CLAIRE R.
Shea School of Art
3258 Overland Ave.
Los Angeles, Ca. 90034 .... *

SHECTER, MARK
1800 N. Charles St.
Baltimore, Md. 21201 144

SHENKER, ILYA
% Ligoa Duncan Gallery
22 E. 72nd St.
New York, N.Y. 10021 144

SHERWOOD, A.
3905 N.W. 37th Pl.
Gainesville, Fl. 32601 145

SHIPMAN, HELEN P.
% Bell Gallery
202 Fieldpoint Rd.
Greenwich, Ct. 06830 145

SIGNOR, EUGENIA H.
204 20th Ave., N.
Jacksonville Beach, Fl. 32250 145

SKINNER, ILENE N.
15232 Iron Canyon Rd.
Canyon Country, Ca. 91351 146

SKLAR, ELLEN E.
P.O. Box 309
Marblehead, Ma. 01945 146

SMALL, FAY
212 E. Broadway
New York, N.Y. 10002 146

SMITH, JAY ALFRED
P.O. Box 4244
N. Hollywood, Ca. 91607 147

SMITH, VERN H.
215 Elm Court
Scotch Plains, N.J. 07076 147

SOLOMON, FREDERICK
New English Art Gallery
Charles St.
Rochester, N.H. 03867 .... *

SOLOMON, SAM
% The Stan Solomon Collection
2501 N.W. 5th Ave.
Miami, Fl. 33127 148

SPRADLEY, WAYNE
911 Hill-Top Rd.
Pell City, Al. 35125 147

STEELE, STEVEN M.
1727 E. Jamison Ave.
Littleton, Co. 80122 149

STEINBERG, SAUL
% Galerie Maeght
13 rue de Teheran
Paris, F-75008, France 149

STICE, BILL
P.O. Box 149
Captiva Island, Fl. 33924 .... *

STOLPIN, WILLIAM R.
12201 Gage Rd.
Holly, MI. 48442 150

STRUEKEN, MARION
50 E. 89th St.
New York, N.Y. 10028 149

SUN, LARS ERIK
242 W. 10th St., Apt. 64
New York, N.Y. 10014 150

SWAYNE, ZOA L.
P.O. Box 786
Orofino, Id. 83544 152

SWITZER, M.A. BAHL
1111 W. Cook Rd.
Mansfield, Oh. 44906 149

SZATHMÁRY, KARA
White Dwarf Studio
Box 295
Dunham, Quebec, Canada J0E 1M0 151

TAMURA, HERO
10242 4th St., N.W.
Albuquerque, N.M. 87114 152

TARDIF-HEBERT
15 Romfield Circuit
Thornhill, Ontario
Canada L3T 3H4 153

TAYLOR, WALTER S.
% Bully Hill Vineyards
Greyton H. Taylor Memorial Dr.
Hammondsport, N.Y. 14840 152

TEABO, SHARON L.
310 Seventh Ave.
Hinton, W.V. 25951 153

THEDICK, LINDA
1557 Charon Rd.
Jacksonville, Fl. 32205 .... *

THIAIS-LOUBRIS
% Ligoa Duncan "Arts"
22 E. 72nd St.
New York, N.Y. 10021 153

THRASHER, JACQUELYN A.
2210 Harvard Ave.
Midland, Tx. 79701 .... *

TOMASI, ADRIAN
6 Greene St.
New York, N.Y. 10013 154

TOMCHUK, MARJORIE
44 Horton La.
New Canaan, Ct. 06840 158

TOMLINSON, RICHARD
319 E. 24th St.
New York, N.Y. 10010 156

TONG, VERA
23 Chatham Sq.
New York, N.Y. 10038 155

TOUTZ, CHARLES F.
2440 34th St.
Santa Monica, Ca. 90405 157

TURNER, JANET E.
567 E. Lassen, Sp. 701
Chico, Ca. 95926 156

TWOMBLY, CY
% Leo Castelli Gallery
420 W. Broadway
New York, N.Y. 10013 158

UNDERWOOD, EVELYN NOTMAN
362 Linden Ave.
E. Aurora, N.Y. 14052 158

URSO, RICHARD CARL
% The Union Art Gallery
349 Geary St.
San Francisco, Ca. 94102 160

UTTER, LOU
P.O. Box 177
Easton, Md. 21601 159

VARES, KEN
208 Goodwin St.
Hayward, Ca. 94544 160

VARZA, IRMA
P.O. Box 204, Parkchester Sta.
New York, N.Y. 10462 .... *

VICTOR, BARRY ALAN
3 Mansion Dr.
Hyde Park, N.Y. 12538 160

VON SZITANYI-WALEWSKA
631 W. 185th St.
New York, N.Y. 10033 161

WALL, PAT
% Tree House Gallery
P.O. Box 310
Langley, Ok. 74350 161

WARD, BETHEA
9614 Val Verde
Houston, Tx. 77063 161

WARHOL, ANDY
Andy Warhol Enterprises
860 Broadway
New York, N.Y. 10003 162

WASHINGTON, JENNI S.
11439 S. Racine St.
Chicago, Il. 60643 161

WATERMAN, LORI
562 Gerona Rd
Stanford, Ca. 94305 163

WATKINS, CURTIS W.
519 S. Michigan
Howell, Mi. 48843 163

WEIL, MEG
240 Central Park South
New York, N.Y. 10019 164

WENNET, ELLIOTT
% The Stan Solomon Collection
2501 N.W. 5th Ave.
Miami, Fl. 33127 165

WESTERMAN, JUNE A.
4947 Habana Dr.
Sarasota, Fl. 33580 .... *

WHITING, PEGGY L.
9805 Pamela Dr.
Temperance, Mi. 48182 164

WILEE, ELIZABETH R.
2415 Dennywood Dr.
Nashville, Tn. 37214 .... *

WILL, S.
P.O. Box 8457
Van Nuys, Ca. 91409 170

WILLIAMS, EVELYN SINGER
479 Walton Ferry Rd.
Hendersonville, Tn. 37075 .... 166, 167

WILNER, MARIE
% Ligoa Duncan "Arts"
22 E. 72nd St.
New York, N.Y. 10021 170

WINDELL, VIOLET BRUNER
R.R. 1, Box 108
Ramsey, In. 47166 168

WOOD, TERESA DALLAPICCOLA
6315 Bartlett St.
Pittsburgh, Pa. 15217 .... *

WOODWARD, DAN & CAROLYN
311 La France Ave.
Alhambra, Ca. 91803 .... *

WOOLFSON, JEAN
2477 Becket Dr.
Union City, Ca. 94587 170

WYETH, JAMES
Chadds Ford, Pa. 19317 169

ZARFOS, GLENN M.
404 Commerce St.
New Cumberland, W.V. 26047 170

ARTISTS/USA   *Directory listing only